Viruses in Water Systems

Detection and Identification

Viruses in Water Systems

Detection and Identification

By
J. C. Block
L. Schwartzbrod

Translated from the French by Luke A. Burke

J. C. Block
Center for Environmental Sciences
1 rue de Recollets
57000 Metz
France

L. Schwartzbrod
Laboratoire de Virologie
Faculte de Pharmacie
5 rue Albert Lebrun
54000 Nancy
France

Library of Congress Cataloging-in-Publication Data

Block, J. C.
    [Analyse virologique des eaux. English]
    Viruses in water systems: detection and identification/J. C.
Block, L. Schwartzbrod.
    p. cm.
    Translation of: Analyse virologique des eaux.
    Includes bibliographies and index.
    ISBN 0-89573-274-2
    1. Viruses—Isolation.   2. Viruses—Identification.   3. Viral
pollution of water.   I. Schwartzbrod, L., 1935– .   II. title.
    [DNLM: 1. Viruses—isolation & purification.   2. Water
Microbiology.   3. Water Supply—analysis.   QW 80 B651a]
QR385.5.B57 1988
616'.0194'028—dc19
DNLM/DLC
for Library of Congress

British Library Cataloguing in Publication Data

Block, J. C.
    Viruses in Water Systems: Detection and Identification
    1. Natural resources. Water. Chemical analysis
    I. Title II. [Analyse virologigue des eaux.
    english]
    628.1'61

ISBN 0-89573-274-2

Originally published as "Analyse Virologique des Eaux" by Technique et Documentation Lavoisier, Paris.

© 1989 VCH Publishers, Inc.

Printed in the United States of America.

ISBN-0-89573-274-2 VCH Publishers
ISBN-3-527-26635-6 VCH Verlagsgesellschaft

Published jointly by:

VCH Publishers, Inc.
220 East 23rd Street
Suite 909
New York, New York 10010

VCH Verlagsgesellschaft mbH
P.O. Box 10 11 16
D-6940 Weinheim
Federal Republic of Germany

TRANSLATOR'S NOTE

At the time that I undertook the translation of Professors Block and Schwartzbrod's book, "Analyse virologique des eaux" there was no equivalent to it in English. Here is a work that presents the techniques needed to start a laboratory for the virological analysis of any water system. It is both a manual and a textbook on the subject, with its succinct cataloguing of waterborne viruses and presentation of the techniques needed for sampling, detection, identification, and quantification of viruses. The level of practicality makes it an ideal introduction to virological analyses for all in the fields of public health, biology, and medicine.

I would like to thank Professor Dennis Joslyn for reading the original translation and correcting the natural bias for terms that I carry with me from Chemistry. I also would like to thank Katherine Sullivan for expertly making all the corrections to the text suggested by the copy editor.

Due to the practicality of this work I have kept the format of the original French version, and, indeed, much of the style—such as short paragraphs for clarity and delineation of text.

Luke A. Burke
Associate Professor of Chemistry
Rutgers—The State University of
New Jersey
Camden, New Jersey 08102

FOREWORD

Roughly 30 years ago the study of viruses in general, and especially of viruses that exist in water, remained the privileged domain of very rare laboratories that were specialized and perfectly equipped. Thus, knowledge of the possible ties between the viruses of human origin and those of the aqueous environment stayed precarious and limited. Since then, the ingenious discovery of Enders, about 1952, and the development of "in vitro" cell cultures that followed, have given way to fabulous progress in virology and a revival of interest in the hypothesis whereby, in analogy with the oldest known basic principles of bacteriology, water might serve as a vehicle and agent of transmission for a good number of viruses that come from fecal excretion.

Since then, a new line of research and study has come into being and has acquired sufficient right to leave the realm of a specialized study and become a full-fledged discipline on a truly international scale.

In reality, before it could assert itself, this specific direction in virology had two problems to resolve: (1) a *sanitary doctrine*, which was to assure that the search for and detection of waterborne viruses was justified and necessary, and (2) a *doctrine of methodology*, which, in case of an affirmative answer to the preceding question, was to be able to master the factors that were limiting access to the virology of water systems, thus providing routine laboratory techniques.

The Problem of a Sanitary Doctrine. There was a time when the risk of waterborne viral contamination seemed to many to be in the realm of fantasy or mere theory, due to the false pretext of its difficult proof. However, the existence of this risk has since been largely proven, and Professor Schwartzbrod was one of those who, in our laboratory, demonstrated its reality in different water systems—and this some 20 years ago! This was a reality that was to be taken into consideration, all the more so since there were two fundamental ideas that later came along: (1) that of a Minimal Infecting Dose (MID), which meant that a sole viral particle meeting cells susceptible to its pathogenic action, in an organism without an immunitary reaction, can provoke an infection, and (2) that of a threshold below which the risk of the presence of such a minimal dose in water becomes negligible.

These ideas, then, dictated and justified a major objective in virological research—the lowering of the threshold for the detection of viral particles.

The Problem of Methodology. Thus, these latter notions led to a closer inspection of the questions of methodology that remained to be solved in order to promote the Virology of Water Systems to the rank of a technique with routine laboratory processes.

vii

These concepts brought up two antagonistic factors—the different types of virus that one is supposed to detect, and the diverse categories of water that serve as vehicles.

Any water following the cycle of wastewater → surface water → potable water is characterized by the quantity of virus that it is capable of containing. Under these conditions the following considerations come into play: (1) the methods of sampling and (2) the volumes taken, with the factor of volume having as a fundamental corollary in viral research the necessity of a concentration step—i.e., using one or several techniques with the major aim of detecting the smallest quantity of virus in the largest possible volume of water. Even if there still do not exist today, among the multitude of methods proposed, one sole method that by its simplicity, ease of execution, sensitivity, reproducibility, and cost can be routinely applied to all categories of water, one must admit that the number of methods has been reduced through fruitful investigations. Thus, one now readily uses the method of adsorption–elution of viral particles on microfibers or on powdered glass, with satisfactory results and without too many technical constraints.

The viral element is just as important to consider, and raises a triple problem of: (1) *number and origin*, as regards the genus and types liable to be formed in water; (2) *techniques* to use in the laboratory, which are often laborious, for the isolation and identification of viruses; and (3) *quantification*, which has as much to do with statistical treatment as with the form of distribution of viral particles throughout the aqueous environment.

It is important to stress here that the virologist confronted with water must above all reckon with what we have called the "fecal hydrovirus," with its morphology and constitution proper to its environment, its resistance and consequently its special virulence and pathogenicity, and also to point out the plasticity of such particles and the technical needs that must be met by a laboratory in order to not only identify but also quantify the viruses.

To these two problems the authors of this work, Professors L. Schwartzbrod and J. C. Block, have each at a given moment in their virological research on water provided answers. Using their profound experience, they have written and edited a document in the production of which everything has been thought out, from the simplest detail, in order to make the task easier and more accessible for those who attempt to follow their lead.

One can only congratulate the authors and hope that the reading of their work provides as much enthusiasm as they had in writing it.

(Translated from French.)
Professor J. M. Foliguet
Biologiste des Hôpitaux
Director of the Laboratoire
   d'Hygiène et de Recherche en
   Santé Publique
Faculté de Médecine B.—Nancy

PREFACE

Protection of public health and a permanent guard on the quality of water systems requires a concern for the viral contamination of the aquatic environment. The combination of developments in research, evolution of techniques, and the emergence of legislation on water quality makes it indispensible that a manual treating the virology of water systems be available to those running analysis laboratories and treatment plants, and to sanitation engineers, physicians, pharmacists, veterinarians, teachers, and their students.

First are presented the viruses found in the aquatic environment and the viral pollution of the diverse categories of water systems. The different steps in a virological analysis of a water system are then taken up, starting with sampling and ending with the quantification and identification of isolated viruses.

The techniques described have been chosen so as to present only those methods that are known to and tested in our laboratories. We have deliberately left out a certain number of techniques that are now in the domain of research or in the course of experimentation.

This book should permit any person interested in the virology of water systems to be able to routinely isolate, quantify, and partially identify the waterborne viruses.

The chapter on the quantification of viruses could not have been written without the close help of Monsieur Maul, to whom we address all our thanks.

We would also like to express our special gratitude to Professors Aymard, Beytout, Festy, and Vilagines and to Doctor Coin, who agreed to read certain chapters and give us their critiques.

The photographs were prepared by Doctors Ferry and Rolland. The micrographs are due to Doctors Georges and Bennani and to Professor Poindron. We thank them very much.

Out thanks also go to Professor Foliguet and to his team, as well as to our coworkers.

We also thank Mesdames Derrez, Nikes, and Pezzotti for their excellent preparation of the original text.

TABLE OF CONTENTS

Chapter 1

WATERBORNE VIRUSES

In the world of microbiology, viruses hold a unique place, somewhere between the realm of living beings and that of macromolecules. The virus is a noncellular entity that possesses little or no enzymatic equipment, no energetic capability, and no machinery for synthesis. It is incapable of reproduction by itself and behaves as an obligatory intracellular parasite. The viruses are tiny particles, sized from 300 to 20 nm.

The simplest of viruses are composed of a nucleic acid, called the genome, which is protected by a protein shell, called the capsid. The genome and the capsid form the nucleocapsid. An additional envelope, which sometimes surrounds the nucleocapsid, constitutes another viral entity.

No matter what kind of virus one is dealing with, its genome is composed of only one type of nucleic acid: RNA or DNA. This constitutes the genetic code belonging to each viral particle (or virion) and permits the multiplication of the virus, which can take place only in the interior of a living cell.

The capsid proteins play several roles in the functioning of the virion. They protect the genome, and they have the property of preferentially fixing themselves onto specific cellular receptors, thus permitting the attachment and penetration of the virus into the cell. Finally, these proteins are antigens; thus they determine the specific antibodies that are made by organisms that become infected.

If the virus has an envelope, it will be a glycolipid protein type, formed from material of cellular origin and material coded by the genetic information of the virus. For certain viruses the envelope has projections resembling spikes. The protein or glycoprotein composition of these spikes imparts a biological activity that is enzymatic, hemagglutinating, or toxic.

The manner in which viruses multiply varies according to viral type and in particular according to nucleic acid type (ie, RNA or DNA). Even so, a viral multiplication cycle can be very generally summarized in six steps:

1. Adsorption or fixation of the virus onto the surface of a susceptible cell
2. Penetration of the virus into the cell
3. Decapsidation and liberation of the genome
4. An eclipse and synthesis phase, during which the viral genome will impose its genetic code on the cellular machinery, causing it to produce viral constituents
5. Assembly of the new viruses in the interior of the cell
6. Liberation of the newly formed viruses

The detection of viruses is difficult by reason of their constitution and also because of their properties. Indeed, they are too small to be observed under the light microscope, and an electron microscope is necessary. Furthermore, since viruses are

Table 1.1. List and classification of the waterborne human viruses

Family	Genera	Principal Species
Picornaviridae	*Enterovirus*	Poliomyelitic virus 1, 2, 3
		Coxsackie virus A_1-A_{22} and A_{24}
		Coxsackie virus B_{1-6}
		ECHO virus 1-9, 11-27, and 29-34
		Enterovirus 68-71
		Hepatitis A virus
		(enterovirus 72)
Reoviridae	*Reovirus*	Reovirus 1, 2, 3
	Rotavirus	Rotavirus 1, 2, 3, 4
Coronaviridae	*Coronavirus*	Human coronaviruses
Caliciviridae	*Calicivirus*	Human caliciviruses
	Astrovirus	Human astroviruses
Adenoviridae	*Mastadenovirus*	Human adenoviruses 1-33
		Norwalk virus
		Hepatitis non-A, non-B virus

Source: After Matthews (1982).

obligatory intracellular parasites, it is not possible to cultivate them on classical bacteriological media.

To isolate and cultivate viruses, they must be put in the presence of living cells in the form of live animals or embryonated eggs or, more often, into in vitro cell cultures. These cultures serve as supports that reveal the presence of a virus by the rather characteristic lesions provoked in the culture when the virus multiplies. This phenomenon of cellular lesions is named the cytopathic effect (CPE).

The principal criteria for classification of viruses are as follows

The nature of the nucleic acid
The type of architecture of the capsid (cubic or helical)
The presence of an envelope around the capsid
The site for intracellular multiplication (cytoplasm or nucleus)
The susceptibility to chemical agents (ether, chloroform, pH, etc)

Also, viruses are distinguished according to whether they infect animals (vertebrates and invertebrates), plants, or bacteria (bacteriophages). Virological studies carried out on water systems, which are the subject of this book, have a bearing mainly on the research and detection of animal viruses and bacteriophages. The viruses most often encountered in environmental waters as well as their place in the classification of viruses are indicated in Table 1.1.

1.1. THE CLASSIFICATION OF VIRUSES IN ENVIRONMENTAL WATERS

1.1.1. Picornaviridae

Within this family (ie, the Picornaviridae), the *Enterovirus* genus represents a large portion of the viruses frequently detected in water. Until now, virological studies of

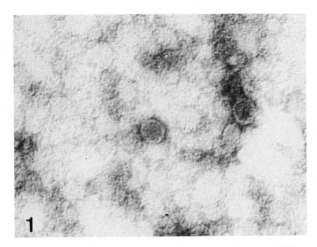

Figure 1.1. Electron micrograph of the poliomyelitic virus (×172,000).

water have concentrated on the search for human enteroviruses. Within this genus, the principal species that are pathogenic for humans are the poliomyelitic, Coxsackie, ECHO, and hepatitis A viruses.

The enteroviruses are small viruses (26–30 nm) with cubic symmetry. They do not possess an envelope (Fig. 1.1). From a structural point of view, they are made up of a single strand of RNA, surrounded by an icosahedral capsid of 60 subunits.

From the point of view of their physical and chemical behavior, enteroviruses are resistant to ether and chloroform (due to the absence of lipids in their capsid) and withstand acids (pH 3). They are conserved very well at −20°C but are inactivated by oxidants (chlorine, bromine, ozone, etc), formaldehyde, propiolactone, and ultraviolet rays.

Antigenic structures are detected by neutralization, complement fixation, assay, and for certain strains of Coxsackie and ECHO virus, by hemagglutination inhibition.

The isolation of these viruses is carried out in vitro on cultures of primate cells. The exceptions to this are for certain Coxsackie A viruses, which can be isolated only on newborn mice and for the hepatitis A virus, which cannot be routinely isolated.

From the epidemiological viewpoint, the transmission of enterovirus infections is essentially interhuman, via an airborne route or by contact with water or foods (shellfish, fruits, vegetables) that have been contaminated by polluted water. This mode of transmission can be explained by considering that in an individual infected clinically or in an unknown way, the virus replicates in the pharynx (and thus will be excreted by the oropharyngeal secretions) and also at the intestinal level, where excretion occurs by way of the stools during a period that can be as long as 3 months.

1.1.1.1. The Poliomyelitic Viruses

The types of poliomyelitic virus are named 1, 2, and 3. The antigenic variations within the same type (ie, intratypic variations) permit the distinction between pathogenic wild strains and vaccinal strains presenting an attenuated character. Differentiation between these variants can be accomplished either in vivo by inoculation of a reference animal, which is the monkey, or in vitro through the use of genetic markers. Isolation can be achieved on primary cell cultures, established lines, or diploid cell lines.

In humans, these viruses are capable of causing acute anterior poliomyelitis, aseptic meningitides, or less defined manifestations marked only by angina, rhinopharyngitis, or digestive troubles. Furthermore, in many cases the infection is unapparent and provokes no clinical manifestation. After the infection (apparent or not), the individual is immunized solely against the type responsible because there is no cross immunity.

1.1.1.2. The Coxsackie Viruses

It is first of all essential to distinguish between the Coxsackie A viruses and the Coxsackie B viruses.

a. Coxsackie A Viruses. Several of the 23 serotypes of Coxsackie A cannot be isolated in vitro on cell cultures. Nevertheless, several strains (eg, RD, MRC 5) arc capable of multiplying on certain types of cell cultures. Classically the isolation of the virus is achieved by inoculation of suckling mice; it provokes febrile paralysis and death within 3 to 10 days.

In humans the Coxsackie A viruses can provoke attacks on the central nervous system and respiratory, ocular, digestive, or cutaneomucous manifestations. Furthermore, they are the agents of vesiculous pharyngitis or herpangina.

b. Coxsackie B Viruses. The six serotypes of Coxsackie B (B_{1-6}) can be isolated on cell cultures (primary cultures of monkey kidney cells or on established lines, eg, BGM) and also can be obtained by inoculation of suckling mice, where they cause the appearance of spasmodic paralyses followed by death in 5 to 10 days.

In humans the Coxsackie B viruses are responsible for the onset of epidemic myalgia, cardiovascular and cutaneomucous manifestations, and attacks on the central nervous system. Also, certain authors estimate that after infection by these viruses, some children might be afflicted with juvenile diabetes (Wilson et al, 1977).

1.1.1.3. ECHO Viruses

The 32 serotypes of the enteric cytopathogenic human orphan (ECHO) virus are developed in vitro in primary cell cultures and in human embryonic cell cultures (MRC 5); with more difficulty they can be obtained on established cell lines.

These viruses are associated with extremely varied infections in humans, ranging from attack on the central nervous system (meningitis) to digestive manifestations (diarrhea) and including attacks on the respiratory system or the ocular (conjunctivitis) system.

1.1.1.4. Hepatitis A Virus

Thus far only one hepatitis A serotype has been detected. Although different strains have been isolated, it has never been possible to detect any antigenic differences between them.

Hepatitis A virus (HAV) is responsible for isolated cases of hepatitis and for small epidemics, but there exist numerous subclinical infections. During the course of an infection, regardless of whether it is detected, the virus is excreted in fecal matter. Excretion commences 7 to 14 days before the appearance of jaundice and appears to reach a maximum at the start of the elevation in serum transaminases, diminishing rapidly in the 7 days that follow the start of the jaundice.

The animals that are sensitive to HAV are two apes: the marmoset and the chimpanzee.

The first culture of HAV on in vitro cell systems was performed in 1978 by Provost and Hilleman, and several teams of researchers have been successful with this culture on several cell lines (FRhK$_4$, FRhK$_6$, AGMK, PLC/PRF/S, etc); but its culture is long and difficult and is not disclosed by any cytopathic effect. Currently then, the virus cannot be routinely isolated on cell cultures.

The detection of HAV in pathological systems is carried out by electron microscopy, electron immunomicroscopy and, above all, by immunological techniques (radioimmunology, immunoenzymology, etc).

1.1.2. Reoviridae

The viruses belonging to the Reoviridae are spread over several genera, three of these—*Reovirus, Rotavirus*, and *Orbivirus*—contain viruses affecting humans. Only the reoviruses and the rotaviruses are capable of transmission through water.

These double stranded RNA viruses have cubic symmetry and varying size from 65 to 80 nm. The nucleic acid is surrounded by an internal capsid and an external capsid. The Reoviridae are resistant to ether and solvents for lipids and are stable at pH3.

1.1.2.1. Reoviruses

Three types of reovirus, namely, types 1, 2, and 3, have been isolated from humans. Their size is 75 nm. The RNA genome is divided into 10 fragments. These viruses can be isolated on different in vitro cell cultures, in which they provoke a cytopathic effect. In humans reoviruses are found in the respiratory and enteric tracts. Their pathogenicity for humans is still under discussion because these viruses have been found during the course of a variety of syndromes, but the relation between infection and disease is not clear. Certain authors (eg Notkins et al, 1981) suspect that they may play a role in the etiology of juvenile diabetes.

1.1.2.2. Rotaviruses

Several *Rotavirus* species have been isolated in humans and in numerous animals. Two subgroups of human rotaviruses have been distinguished, with a total of four serotypes (Wyatt et al, 1983).

As observed in electron microscopy, the viral particle resembles a wheel whose axle is represented by the central nucleus, the spokes by the subunits of the internal capsid, and the rim by the external capsid (Champsaur, 1985). The size is around 70 nm (Fig. 1.2).

The in vitro culture on cell systems of human rotaviruses is not easy. It is most often attempted on MA 104 cells with the addition of trypsin (Kasegawa et al, 1982) to

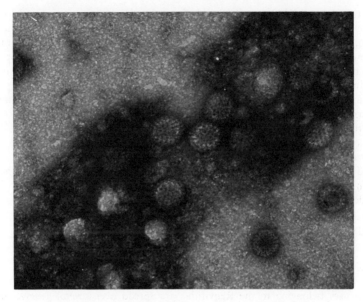

Figure 1.2. Electron micrograph of the rotavirus (×150,000).

the culture medium, since this enzyme cleaves a capsid protein, which secondarily facilitates the intracellular decapsidation of the virus.

The rotaviruses are classically detected by electron microscope and by immunological methods of the immunoenzymatic type (eg, enzyme linked immunoadsorbent assay: ELISA) or by radioimmunology. They can be considered to be one of the major etiological agents in infantile gastroenteritis and may be responsible for nearly 2 million deaths per year in developing countries. They provoke small epidemics, above all in hospital services and nurseries. There is a seasonal prevalence that is very marked during the coldest months of the year in temperate countries (Champsaur et al, 1984).

1.1.3. Coronaviridae

Coronaviruses occur in the form of irregularly enveloped particles whose average diameter varies from 75 to 160 nm. The envelope contains club-shaped projections that give these viruses their characteristic form of a crown (Fig. 1.3). The nucleic acid constituting the genome is a single strand of RNA. These viruses are degraded by ether, chloroform, and detergents.

First found during the course of pathological manifestations in the respiratory branch, the coronaviruses were then isolated during enteric troubles in animals, and later observed in human stools by Caul et al (1975). They were then found to be responsible for severe hemorrhagic gastroenteritis in children (Vaucher et al, 1982). Some strains are capable of multiplying on cell cultures of human rectal adenocarcinomas (HRT 18 line) (Laporte et al, 1980), on which they do not provoke a cytopathic effect in liquid medium but give plaques under gel agar overlay. However, their detection is performed essentially by microscopic examination and by electron immunomicroscopy.

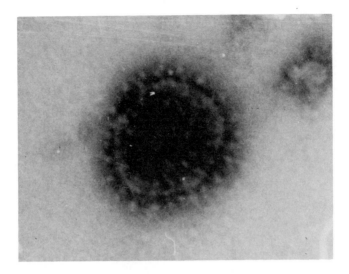

Figure 1.3. Electron micrograph of the coronavirus (× 240,000).

1.1.4. Caliciviridae

The caliciviruses are small viruses without envelopes, having a diameter between 30 and 38 nm and occurring in roughly spherical form with 32 capsomers. They are single stranded RNA viruses that are not destroyed by chloroform but are inactivated between ph 3 and 5. They do not multiply on in vitro cell cultures. They were first observed by electron microscopy (Flewett and Davies, 1976), then by electron immunomicroscopy in the stools of children suffering from gastroenteritis (Madeley and Cosgrove, 1976). The disease is in general benign. According to Chiva et al (1980), the period of viral excretion is relatively short, since although the viruses are found in the stools of 100% of the patients for the first 4 days of the disease, they are present in the stools of only 50% of the subjects between days 5 and 9.

1.1.5. Astroviridae

Discovered by Madeley and Cosgrove (1975), the astroviruses are revealed by electron microscopy to have a starlike appearance with five or six branches. Their size is from 28 to 30 nm, and they are believed to be single stranded RNA viruses. Detected in the stools of children by electron microscopy and immunomicroscopy, they may be responsible for gastroenteritis occurring principally in children; however epidemiological studies have shown that secondary cases are not rare and might affect adults (Konno et al, 1982).

1.1.6. Adenoviridae

The adenoviruses have cubic symmetry and vary in size from 70 to 90 nm. They do not possess an envelope. They are composed of double-stranded DNA enclosed in an icosahedral capsid formed by the assemblage of 252 capsomers. The 12 capsomers

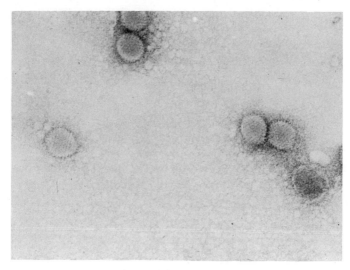

Figure 1.4. Electron micrograph of the type 7 adenovirus (×120,000).

situated at the apices of the icosahedron support filamentous projections that have hemagglutinating properties (Fig. 1.4). Adenoviruses are resistant to ether and chloroform, can support rather large variations in pH, and are well preserved by freezing at −20°C.

There are two genera in the family of adenoviruses, but only *Mastadenovirus* is detailed here. This genus contains the viruses responsible for infections in mammals, and within it, alongside the viruses proper to animals, 33 human serotypes have been described.

Isolation of these viruses can be accomplished by the inoculation of diverse categories of human cell cultures.

Immunologically, the adenoviruses possess a hemagglutinin. Certain among them agglutinate the red blood cells of monkeys, and others agglutinate rat red blood corpuscles. These hemagglutinating properties permit differentiation of the viruses.

Pathogenically, the mastadenoviruses are responsible for diverse infections and syndromes in man that particularly affect the respiratory tract, the eye (conjunctivitis, keratoconjunctivitis), and the intestinal tract (acute mesenteric adenitis). Often, these infections are banal and unapparent, but they are very widespread.

In the course of these infections, manifested or not, the viruses multiply in the affected organs, which is why they are frequently recovered in the rhinopharyngeal secretions and in feces. The fecal excretion takes place during the 3 to 4 weeks following the infection.

1.1.7. Norwalk and Similar Viruses

The Norwalk virus was detected after an epidemic of gastroenteritis in Norwalk, Ohio, in 1969, and was reported by Kapikian et al (1972). It has the form of particles 25 to 27 nm in diameter. The nature of its genome has not been determined, and it has yet to be cultivated in vitro.

Several other agents morphologically similar to this virus have been described as agents of gastroenteritis: the Hawaii agent (Thornhill et al, 1977), that of Montgomery

County (Appleton et al, 1977), the Otofuke agent (Taniguchi et al, 1979), and the Sapporo agent (Kogasaka et al, 1981).

The Norwalk virus and the other infectious agents were detected by electron microscopy and immunomicroscopy. They are responsible for brief (12–24 hour) gastroenteritic syndromes manifested by nausea, vomiting, and diarrhea.

1.1.8. Non-A and non-B Hepatitis Viruses

The term "non-A, non-B hepatitis" includes viral hepatitides which are serologically unrelated to the hepatitis A and hepatitis B viruses. Given the attempts at experimental transmission, it seems there exist at least two non-A and non-B hepatitides with different etiologies (Deinhardt and Gust, 1983).

One presents symptoms that are similar to those of hepatitis B and might be provoked by a B-like virus (ie, a DNA virus of around 42 nm).

The other presents close similarities from the clinical point of view with hepatitis A and might be due to an A-like virus (ie, an RNA virus of around 27 nm). The disease seems to be transmitted by the orofecal path, affecting above all children and young adults and possibly provoking geographically limited epidemics (Deinhardt and Gust, 1983). This virus has not yet been cultivated.

1.2. VIRAL CONTAMINATION OF WATER

Technological developments, the rise in living standards, and the concentration of populations into zones of high density during the past few decades have necessitated the diversification of sources of drinking water. Surface water has come to be added more and more to subterranean water. However, surface waters receive urban wastewaters contaminated with fecal material, thus increasing the risk of viral contamination (Fig. 1.5).

Since the viruses described previously are eliminated in the feces, it is easy to show the viral contamination of water systems. Thus contaminated water systems can be the origin of infections obtained after eating shellfish and after the absorption of water not only in drinks and ice but on washed vegetables and fruits, as well. Infections also can be contracted after ingestion of water during swimming, windsurfing, and other such activities.

Viral contamination is far from being quantitatively negligible. Indeed, individuals stricken by a clinically evident viral infection, as well as those who develop subclinical infections, eliminate important quantities of viruses. As shown by Clarke (1961), if one takes a normal population to consist of 70% adults and 30% children, the average level of viral excretion is around 300 particles per gram of stool. This corresponds to around 60,000 viral particles excreted per day per inhabitant of an urban community. Humans should thus be considered to be the disseminators capable of contaminating the whole of the water environment through their wastewater (Fig 1.5).

1.2.1. Viral Contamination of Wastewater

In the raw wastewater that constitutes the natural receptacle for fecal matter, it is logical for the viral concentration to be very high. Some values are presented in Table 1.2.

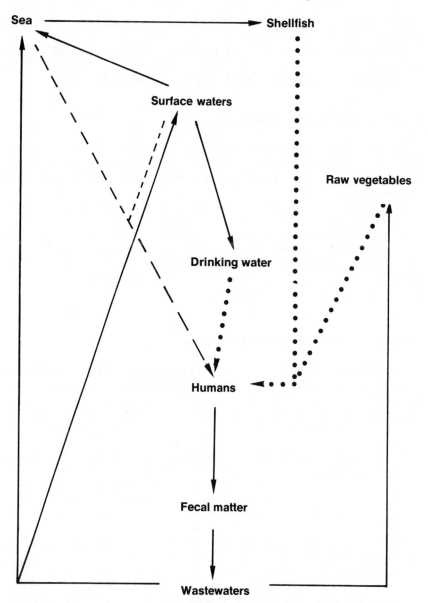

Figure 1.5. Pathways for viral contamination of humans by fecal matter and wastewaters: _____ contamination of the environment by humans, _ _ _ _ contamination of humans during their activities, ... contamination of humans by food.

In fact, the quantity of viruses present in wastewater varies as a function of numerous factors: geographic, socioeconomic, sanitary, and seasonal. Thus, Bitton et al (1985) demonstrated that the concentration of enteroviruses varies at least from 1 to 20,000 particles per liter.

According to country, wastewaters either undergo a purification treatment required by law or are discharged directly into the environment (rivers, lakes, seas, and also into

Table 1.2. Viruses isolated from raw wastewater

Viral concentration per liter[a]	Type of virus isolated[b]	Reference
10-350 PFU	Entero	Block et al, 1979
36-4600 MPNCU	Entero	Schwartzbrod et al, 1979
12-74 PFU	CB_{2-3}; Rota; HAV antiges	Hejkal et al, 1982
120-9140 PFU	P_{1-3}; CB_{2-6}	Slade, 1982
< 50 PFU	P_{1-3}; CB_{2-5}; $E_{1,7,11}$; Reo; Adeno	Payment et al, 1983
< 1-3300 PFU	P_{1-3}; CA_{16}; $CB_{1,2,4,5}$ $E_{5,7,9,13-15,18,20}$ $_{21,24,25,27,29,30}$	Martins et al, 1983
ND	P_{1-3}; $CB_{2,3,5}$; $E_{1,6,7,11}$; $E_{16,31}$; Reo2	Agbalika et al, 1983
100-1000 PFU	P_3; CB_5; E_7	Krikelis et al, 1984
250-3000 $TCID_{50}$	$P_{1,2}$; CB_4; E_{5-7}	Farrah, 1985

[a] Key: MPNCU = most probable number of cytopathic units
                ND = not determined
                PFU = plaque-forming units
                $TCID_{50}$ = dose that infects 50% of tissue cultures
[b] Key: Adeno = adenovirus
            CA = Coxsackie A virus
            CB = Coxsackie B virus
             E = ECHO virus
    Entero = enterovirus
        HAV = hepatitis A virus
              P = poliovirus
         Reo = reovirus
        Rota = rotavirus

the soil, by spreading, irrigation, or aspersion). In fact, physicochemical techniques or biological procedures such as activated sludge permit the elimination of between 50 and 90% of the viruses present. Under these conditions, the viral load is relatively small (cf Table 1.3) but not negligible, because the volumes of wastewater are very large. Thus, a wastewater treatment plant for an urban community of 300,000 inhabitants producing 150,000 cubic meters of wastewater per day discharges a minimum of 10^9 viral particles into a river every 24 hours (Schwartzbrod et al, 1979).

Table 1.3. Viruses isolated from treated wastewaters[a]

Viral concentration per liter	Type of virus isolated	Reference
0-30 PFU	Entero	Payment et al, 1979
0-9.6 MPNCU	Entero	Schwartzbrod et al, 1979
2.7-29 MPNCU	Entero	Joret et al, 1980
0.1-91 MPNCU	$P_{2,3}$; CB_4; E_{24}	Maurin and Demillac, 1981
0-180 PFU	$P_{1,2}$; CB_{3-5}	Slade, 1982
2-353 PFU	P_{1-3}; $CB_{2,5}$	Simmonds et al, 1983

[a] See Table 1.2 for keys to abbreviations.

Table 1.4. Viruses isolated from river water[a]

Viral concentration per liter	Type of virus isolated	River	References
0–283 PFU	Entero	Rhine (France)	Block et al, 1978
ND	$P_{1,3}$; $CB_{4,5}$; $E_{7,11}$	Danube (Rumania)	Nestor et al, 1981
18 → 55 MPNCU	Entero	Rio Besos (Spain)	Lucena et al, 1982
0.44–44 MPNCU	Entero	Rio Llobregat (Spain)	Lucena et al, 1982
0.15–4.5 MPNCU	P_2; $CB_{4,5}$; $E_{7,1}$	Loier (France)	Le Bris et al, 1983

[a] See Table 1.2 for keys to abbreviations.

1.2.2. Viral Contamination of Recreational Waters

Certain natural physical or chemical factors serve to diminish the viral concentration in surface waters (Block, 1983). Thus, dilution in the environment provokes a lowering of the viral concentration. Also, factors such as sunshine, elevated temperature, bacterial activity, and oxygenation provoke or favor viral inactivation. However, it is essential to note that viruses can be protected from inactivating agents by adsorption on particles present in waters. The quantities of virus found in rivers and streams are sometimes still relatively large, as can be seen from the results collected in Table 1.4.

In seawater, however, the quantities of virus are clearly smaller, as indicated in Table 1.5, but viral particles are still found in certain cases up to 5 km from the wastewater discharge point.

From Tables 1.4 and 1.5 it is entirely clear that recreational waters such as seawater and rivers often contain small but nonnegligible quantities of viral particles. The same can be said for swimming pool water, as indicated by the results in Table 1.6.

Table 1.5. Viruses isolated from seawater[a]

Viral concentration per liter	Type of virus isolated	Sea	References
< 0.05–6.5 MPNCU	CA_{21}; E_{11}; $Adeno_6$	Mediterranean (France)	Hugues et al, 1980
0.12–1.72 MPNCU	P_{1-3}; CB_5	Mediterranean (Spain)	Finance et al, 1982
0.1–0.8 PFU	$P_{1,2}$; $CB_{2,4,5}$; $E_{4,11}$	Irish Sea	Tyler, 1982
0.05–1.35 PFU	$P_{1,2}$; E_{24}	Atlantic (Brazil)	Marques and Martins, 1983
0.006–0.026 PFU	P_2; E_{7-29}	Gulf of Mexico (USA)	Rao et al 1984,

[a] See Table 1.2 for keys to abbreviations.

Table 1.6. Viruses isolated from swimming pool water[a]

Type of virus isolated	Proportion of positive samples	Reference
Entero	ND	Hugues et al, 1979
CB_6; $E_{6,7}$	ND	Marzouk et al, 1980
P_1; $CB_{3,4}$; E_7	71.4%	Keswick et al, 1981
P_1; CB_3; Reo	30.9%	Prevot et al, 1983
CA; CB; E	28.4%	Cotor et al, 1983
$P_{1,2}$; E_7; Reo	ND	Festy, 1984

[a]See Table 1.2 for keys to abbreviations.

1.2.3. Viral Contamination of Water Distribution Systems

Drinking water makes up the third component in the water cycle. As so much drinking water is obtained from contaminated surface water, it is obvious that treatments applied to these waters must be completely trustworthy if viral contamination of water delivered for consumption is to be avoided. Very considerable efforts have been made to bring on line techniques that are capable of eliminating all pathogenic microorganisms. However, in developing countries these treatments often do not exist or, sometimes, are defective. Even so, in numerous countries such as Canada, the United States, France, Romania, and the Soviet Union, some viral particles have been isolated in treated waters that are distributed to the population (Table 1.7).

In general the detection of viruses in drinking water is carried out with large volumes, and quantification is rarely performed.

1.3. EPIDEMIOLOGY

It is difficult to estimate the respective roles of bacteria and viruses in the pathology connected with the consumption of contaminated waters because only a certain number of fragmentary studies have treated this problem. According to Cliver (1984), epidemics of viral origin catalogued in the United States between 1975 and 1979 (Table

Table 1.7. Viruses isolated from potable water systems

Type of virus isolated	Origin of the water	Reference
P_{1-3}; C; E	Surface water	Coin et al, 1965
P	Surface water	Drozdov and Kasantseva, 1978
P_2; CA_4	Surface water	Nestor et al, 1978
P_1	Surface water	Payment, 1981
P_{1-3}; CA; CB_4; E_{11}	Surface water	Festy, 1984
$P_{1,2}$; CB_5; Reo 1	Ground water	Festy, 1984
CB_{3-6}; Rota	Surface water	Deetz et al, 1984
Reo	Spring water	Schwartzbrod et al, 1985

[a]See Table 1.2 for keys to abbreviations.

Table 1.8. Epidemic episodes connected with water in the
United States, 1975–1979

Total number	Confirmed etiology	Viral etiology
170 epidemics	39%	4.7%
41,083 cases	54.5%	3.2%

Source: Cliver (1984).

1.8) might make up only around 5% of all the epidemics that have been tied to water systems. The principal viruses might be those of hepatitis A and of the gastroenteritides, particularly the Norwalk virus.

1.3.1. The Accepted Epidemiological Facts

It is important to point out right away a considerable hiatus between the epidemiological evidence reported in the literature and direct analytical evidence, that is, the detection of the infectious viral agent in water (Karaganis et al, 1983). The amount of epidemiological evidence available is smaller for viruses that are easily isolated in water such as the poliomyelitic, Coxsackie, and ECHO viruses, and to a lesser degree the adenoviruses and reoviruses. However, epidemics provoked by hepatitis A, Norwalk viruses, or viruses responsible for gastroenteritis are clearly confirmed by epidemiological or serological inquests but rarely by the detection of the etiological agent in the waters. Under these conditions the enteroviruses (besides HAV) appear above all as the indicators of viral contamination of water and of the risk associated with the consumption of water from the contaminated source (Table 1.9).

1.3.1.1. Poliomyelitic, Coxsackie, and ECHO Viruses

Although easily and systematically isolated from wastewaters and river waters (Aymard and Brigaud, 1977), the poliomyelitic, Coxsackie, and ECHO viruses appear, at least in the most industrialized countries, only as indicators of viral contamination. In fact, epidemiological proofs of infection contracted by a human from contaminated waters are very rare. Thus, since 1950, no case of poliomyelitis by the water route has been reported in Europe. This is due not only to a campaign of vaccination against the disease, but also to the protection of water resources and to the appropriate treatment of potable water. The Coxsackie viruses have been clearly implicated in a recent epidemic (Hejkal et al, 1980) having as its origin a potable water source contaminated by Coxsackie B_2 and B_3 viruses. An epidemic episode implicating an ECHO 4 virus has caused 80 cases of aseptic meningitis (Cliver, 1984). Information on the transmission to humans of these viruses by the water route is thus very restricted.

1.3.1.2. The Hepatitis A Virus

The study of different epidemics has permitted the confirmation of the importance on the one hand of the water environment and on the other of soiled foods in the

Table 1.9. Viruses isolated from the environment (water and foodstuffs) or responsible for epidemics transmitted by water[a]

Virus	Direct analytical evidence	Epidemiological evidence
Picornaviridae		
Poliomyelitic viruses	+	(+)
Coxsackie virus	+	(+)
Echovirus	+	(+)
Hepatitis A virus	(+)	+ +
Hepatitis non-A, non-B virus	?	+
Reoviridae		
Reoviris	+	?
Rotavirus	(+)	+
Adenovirus	+	+
Norwalk virus	?		
Other viruses responsible for gastroenteritides	?	+

[a] Key: +, + + = large body of information
(+) = fewer reports
? = no information

transmission of hepatitis A virus (World Health Organization, 1979). Although difficult to isolate, this virus has been detected recently in wastewaters and even in water distribution systems (Hejkal et al, 1982; Linglof et al, cited by Dufour, 1983).

Some feel that the rate of incidents of hepatitis A is related to the socioeconomic level of the population and to the type of water distribution system, with the poorest groups having the highest incidence. One must remain cautious, however. In fact, Batik et al (1980) have tried to correlate hepatitis A with potable water distribution system type. This work involved 11,633 cases of hepatitis reported between 1965 and 1970, and took into account population density, and the age, socioeconomic level, and education of the people. At the end of this study the authors could not establish a correlation between the cases of hepatitis A and the supply of potable water or the socioeconomic level of the population.

According to Cliver (1984), in 160,203 declared cases of hepatitis A in the United States from 1975 to 1979, around 4% may have involved transmission by a water route. Among these epidemics of hydrous origin, 80% were due to absence of or deficiency in the treatment of the water. Also, Vilim et al (1977) have reported 24 cases of hepatitis A among 180 residents of a vacation village whose drinking water came from a well contaminated by wastewater. Furthermore, an epidemic occurring in India in the province of Maharashtra (Newaskar et al, 1978) could be connected with the contamination of the water distribution system by wastewater. Such incidences of contamination of water systems are also found in industrialized countries (Bowen and McCarty, 1983).

The hepatitis A virus can be transmitted by the consumption of contaminated food products. Thus, Cliver (1984) considers that in the United States, food is responsible for 10 times more epidemics than water. According to Levin (1978) at least 8.6% of the reported cases of hepatitis A in the United States are associated with the consumption of shellfish that was raw, insufficiently cooked, or not inspected (Goh et al, 1984). In fact, numerous pieces of epidemiological evidence support the transmission of hepatitis A directly or, especially, indirectly by the water route.

1.3.1.3. Non-A, Non-B Hepatitis Viruses

The wastewater-contaminated water distribution systems in New Delhi, India, caused more than 30,000 cases of hepatitis between December 1955 and January 1956 (Viswanathan, 1957). This epidemic was first thought to be provoked by the hepatitis A virus. After a retrospective serological study, however,it was attributed to a non-A, non-B hepatitis virus (Wong et al, 1980). An epidemic of water origin that occurred in Kashmir, India (Khuroo, 1980), and provoked 270 individual cases of hepatitis and 35 secondary contaminations in a population of 17,000 inhabitants, was attributed after an immunological inquest to a non-A, non-B hepatitis virus. Finally, an epidemic that occurred in February and March of 1981 in the Maharashtra, India, might have provoked 1200 cases of jaundice (Sreenivasan et al, 1984). The oral-fecal transmission of these viruses via a water route now seems to be well established.

1.3.1.4. Reoviruses and Rotaviruses

The reoviruses and rotaviruses have been found in almost every human population, but their epidemiology is not well understood. They have rarely been reported in wastewaters or in water distribution systems (Hejkal et al, 1982; Smith and Gerba, 1982) but this is in large part because they are difficult to isolate. They have been indicated in about 10 epidemics of hydrous origin in Europe as well as in the United States (Dufour, 1983; Gerba, 1985).

1.3.1.5. Adenoviruses

Adenoviruses have been suspected sporadically in the transmission of infections by way of swimming pools (Foy et al, 1968; D'Angelo et al, 1979; Payne et al, 1984). However, in many cases, the interhuman transmission that is possible in lockerrooms and in showers remains without doubt the predominant factor.

1.3.1.6. Norwalk Virus

According to the researchers at the U.S. Centers for Disease Control (CDC), around 23% of the epidemics transmitted by water and 4% of the epidemics transmitted by food may be caused by the Norwalk virus or closely related infectious agents (Kaplan et al, 1982). To illustrate, we mention an epidemic of gastroenteritis that struck the children and teachers in a primary school in Tacoma, Washington, in May 1978, with an attack rate as high as 72%. A serological study demonstrated that the agent responsible could have been the Norwalk virus, transmitted by drinking water that had

Table 1.10. Minimal infecting dose[a]

Dose	Virus	Biological System	Rate of Infection	Reference
10 CPD$_{50}$	Poliovirus	Children	67%	Katz and Plotkin, 1967
72 CPD$_{50}$	Poliovirus	Children	50%	Minor et al, 1981
1800–2500 PFU	EP$_3$	Piglets	63%	Cliver, 1981
600–750 PFU	EP$_7$	Piglets	63%	Cliver, 1981
100 PFU	ECHO 12	Students	67%	Schiff et al 1984

[a] Key: CPD$_{50}$ = cytopathic dose destroying 50% of the cell cultures
        PFU = plaque-forming unit

been contaminated by wastewater (Dufour, 1982). Also, an epidemic of severe gastroenteritis had been reported in a vacation camp in North Carolina (Lippy, 1980). The agent responsible for the 146 cases of gastroenteritis among the 186 visitors who had drunk the water from the distribution network might have been a virus of the Norwalk type.

In fact, numerous cases of gastroenteritis that were provoked by drinking water can be connected with Norwalk viruses (Gerba, 1985). Yet, a particular etiological agent cannot be systematically identified in the epidemics. The frequent use of the general term "gastroenteritis viruses" demonstrates the absence of precise knowledge in this domain (Bishop, 1982).

1.3.2 The Minimal Infecting Dose

For a virus to multiply in a human organism, the individual must ingest a minimum quantity of viral particles. This quantity, the minimal infecting dose, depends on numerous parameters such as the type of virus, the state of dispersion of the viral suspension, the food (nature, pH, etc) with which the particles were ingested, and the age and state of immunity of the host (Ward and Akin, 1984).

These different parameters explain without doubt the relative variations in the minimal infecting doses that are described in the literature. For certain authors, human infection can be provoked by one sole infecting unit (reported by the World Health Organization, 1979). All the same, more recent studies carried out on children, young adults, or young pigs (Table 1.10) show that at least 100 viral particles (or aggregates of viruses) are necessary to provoke an infection in the receptor host.

The role and the importance of contaminated water as a vector of viral diseases should be considered in the light of these diverse laboratory observations. In fact, the enteric viruses, which are incapable of multiplying in water, probably should be present in large quantities in environmental waters if they are to be considered to be the origin of an infection or an epidemic. The hypothesis that some who drink water with only a few viral particles per several cubic meters of water have become contaminated by it is still very controversial (International Association of Water Pollutions Research Counsels, 1983). On the other hand, shellfish such as oysters and mussels, which are capable of concentrating the viruses present in water, are very often incriminated in the transmission of viral diseases.

REFERENCES

Agbalika, F., Hartemann, P., Brigaud, M. and Foliguet, J. M. (1983) Circulation des enterovirus dans les eaux usées de la region lorraine. Bilan de la surveillance au cours de la periode 1976–1981. *Rev. Epidemiol. Santé Publique*, **31**, 209–221.

Appleton, H., Buckley, M., Swaminathan, S. P., Yesudass, S. and Baker, S. D. (1977) Virus-like particle in winter vomitingdisease. *Lancet*, **1**, 409–411.

Aymard, M. and Brigaud, M. (1977) Organisation de la surveillance de la circulation des enterovirus dans les eaux d'égout. *Rev. Epidemiol. Santé Publique*, **25**, 469–482.

Batik, O., Craun, G. F., Tuthill, R. W., and Kraemer, D. F. (1980) An epidemiologic study of the relationship between hepatitis and water supply characteristics and treatment. *Am. J. Public Health*, **70**, 167–168.

Bishop, R. F. (1982) Other small virus-like particles in humans. In "Virus Infections of the Gastrointestinal Tract," D. A. J. Tyrrel and A. Z. Kapikian, Eds. Dekker, New York, pp. 199–209.

Bitton, G., Farrah, S. R., Montague, C., Binford, M. W., Scheverman, P. R., and Watson, A. (1985) "Survey of Virus Isolation Data from Environmental Samples." Health Effects Research Laboratory, U.S. Environmental Protection Agency, Cincinatti, OH, 171 pp.

Block, J. C. (1983) Viruses in environmental waters. In "Viral Pollution of the Environment," G. Berg Ed. C. R. C. Press, Boca Raton, FL, pp. 118–145.

Block, J. C., Collin, J. F., Joret, J. C., Rolland, D. and Foliguet, J. M. (1979) Elimination des enterovirus au cours du traitement par boues activées des eaux usées urbaines. *Tech. Sci. Munic.* **74**, 201–206.

Block, J. C., Joret, J. C., Morlot, M. and Foliguet, J. M. (1978) Recherche des enterovirus dans les eaux superficielles par adsorption elution sur microfibre de verre. *Tech. Sci. Munic.* **73**, 181–185.

Bowen, G. S., and McCarty, M. A. (1983) Hepatitis A associated with a hardware store water fountain and a contaminated well in Lancaster County, Pennsylvania, 1980. *Am. J. Epidemiol.* **117**, 695–705.

Caul, E. O., Pauer, W. K., and Clarcke, S. K. R. (1975) Coronavirus particles in faeces from patients with gastroenteritis. *Lancet*, **1**, 1192.

Champsaur, H. (1985) Les Reovirides: Reovirus et rotavirus. In "Virologie Medicale," J. Maurin, Ed. Flammarion, Paris, pp. 716–735.

Champsaur, H., Questiaux, E., Prevot, J., Henry-Amad, M., Goldszmidt, D., Bourjouane, M. and Bach, C. (1984) Rotavirus carriage, asymptomatic infection and disease in the first two years. I. Virus shedding study. *J. Infect. Dis.* **149**, 667–674.

Chiba, S., Sakuma, Y., Kogasaka, R., Akihara, M., Terashima, H., Horino, K., and Nakao, T. (1980) Fecal shedding of virus in relation to the days of illness in infantile gastroenteritis due to calicivirus. *J. Infect. Dis.* **142**, 247–249.

Clarke, N.A. (1961) Removal of enteric viruses from sewage by activated sludge treatment. *Am. J. Public Health*, **51**, 1118–1120.

Cliver, D. O. (1984) Significance of water and the environment in the transmission of virus disease. In "Enteric viruses in water," no. 15 of Monographs in Virology, 15, J. L. Melnick, Ed. Karger, Basle, pp. 30–42.

Cliver, D. O. (1981) Experimental infection by waterborne enteroviruses. *J. Food Protect.* **44**, 861–869.

Coin, L., Menetrier, M. L., Labonde, J., and Hannoun, M. C. (1965) Modern microbiological and virological aspects of water pollution. In "Advances in Water Pollution Research," O. Jaag and J. K. Baars, Eds. Pergamon Press, Oxford.

Cotor, F., Zavate, O., Finichiu, M., Avram, G., and Ivan, A. (1983) Enterovirus contamination of swimming pool water: Correlation with bacteriological indicators. *Rev. Roum. Med. Virol.* **34**, 251–256.

D'Angelo, L. J., Hierholzer, J. C., Keenlyside, R. A., Anderson, L. J., and Mortone, W. J. (1979) Pharyngoconjunctival fever caused by adenovirus type 4: Report of a swimming pool-related outbreak with recovery of virus from pool water. *J. Infect. Dis.* **140**, 42–47.

Deetz, T. R., Smith, E. M., Goyal, S. M., Gerba, C. P., Vollet, J. J., Tsai, L., Dupont, H. L., and Keswick, B. H. (1984) Occurrence of rota- and enteroviruses in drinking and environmental waters in a developing nation. *Water Res.* **18**, 567–572.

Deinhardt, F. and Gust, I. D. (1983) L'hepatite virale. *Bull. Organ. Mond. Sante*, **61**, 193–232.

Drozdov, S. G., and Kasantseva, V. A. (1978) Detection of viruses in sewage, surface and tap waters: Effectiveness of treatment in removal of viruses. Fourth International Congress of Virology, The Hague.

Dufour, A. P. (1983) Disease outbreaks caused by drinking water. *J. Water Pollut. Control Fed.* **55**, 905–908.

Dufour, A. P. (1982) Disease outbreaks caused by drinking water. *J. Water Pollut. Control Fed.* **54**, 980–983.

Farrah, S. R. (1985) In "Survey of Virus Isolation Data from Environmental Samples," G. Bitton, S. R. Farrah, C. Montague, M. W. Binford, P. R. Scheverman, and A. Watson, Eds. Health Effects Research Laboratory, U.S. Envirmonental Protection Agency, Cincinnati, OH, 171 pp.

Festy, B. (1984) In "Survey of Virus Isolation Data from Environmental Samples," G. Bitton, S. R. Farrah, C. Montague, M. W. Binford, P. R. Scheverman, and A. Watson, Eds. Health Effects Research Laboratory, U.S. Environmental Protection Agency, Cincinnati, OH, 171 pp.

Finance, C., Lucena, F., Brigaud, M., Aymard, M., Pares, R. and Schwartzbrod, L. (1982) Etude quantitative et qualitative de la pollution virale de l'eau de mer a Barcelone. *Rev. Fr. Sci. Eau*, **1**, 139–149.

Flewett, T. H., and Davies, H. (1976) Caliciviruses in man. *Lancet*, 1, 311.

Foy, H. M., Cooney, M. K., and Hatlen, J. B. (1968) Adenovirus type 3 epidemic associated with intermittent chlorination of a swimming pool. *Arch. Environ. Health*, **17**, 795–802.

Gerba, C. P. (1985) Waterborne gastroenteritis and viral hepatitis. *C. R. C. Crit. Rev. Environ. Control*, **15**, 213–236.

Goh, K. T., Chan, L., Ding, J. L., and Oon, C. J. (1984) An epidemic of cockles)associated hepatitis A in Singapore. *Bull. World Health Organ.* **62**, 893–897.

Hejkal, T., Keswick, B., Labelle, R., Gerba, C., Sanchez Y., Dreesman, G., Hafkin, B., and Melnick, J. L. (1982) Viruses in a community water supply associated with an outbreak of gastroenteritis and infectious hepatitis. *J. Am. Waterworks Assoc.* **74**, 318–321.

Hugues, B., Cini, A., Plissier, M., and Lefebvre, J. R. (1980) Recherche des virus dans le milieu marin a partir d'echantillons de volumes differents. *Eau Quebec*, **13**, 199–203.

Hugues, B., Plissier, M., Mothon, F., and Bocquet, J. P. (1979) Recherche virale dans les zones recreatives. *Rev. Fr. Sante Publique*, **7**, 53–61.

International Association of Water Pollution Research Councils Study Group on Water Virology (1983) The health significance of viruses in water. *Water Res.* **17**, 121–132.

Joret, J. C., Block, J. C., Lucena, F., Schwartzbrod, L., Hugues, B., and Plissier, M. (1980) Virus concentration from secondary wastewater: Comparative study between epoxy fiberglass and glass powder adsorbents. *Eur. J. Appl. Microbiol. Biotechnol.* **10**, 245–252.

Kapikian, A. Z., Wyatt, R. G., Dolin, R., Thornhill. T. S., Kalica, A. R., and Chanock, R. M. (1972) Visualization by immune electron microscopy of a 27 nm particle associated with acute infectious nonbacterial gastroenteritis. *J. Virol.* **10**, 1075–1081.

Kaplan, J. E., Feldman, R., Campbell, D. S., Lookabaugh, C., and Gary, G. W. (1982). The frequency of a Norwalk)like pattern of illness in outbreaks of acute gastroenteritis. *Am. J. Public Health*, **72**, 1329–1332.

Karaganis, J. V., Larkin, E. P., Melnick, J. L., Scarpino, P. V., Schaub, S. A., Sorber, C. A., Sullivan, R., and Wellings, F. M. (1983) Research priorities for monitoring viruses in the environment. U.S. Environmental Protection Agency Report 600/9-83-010. E.P.A., Cincinnati, OH, 12 pp.

Kasegawa, A., Matsuno, S., Inouye, S., Kono, R., Tsurukubo, Y., Mukoyama, A., and Saito, Y. (1982) Isolation of human rotaviruses in primary cultures of monkey kidney cells. *J. Clin. Microbiol.* **16**, 387–390.

Katz, M., and Plotkin, S. A. (1967) Animal infective dose of attenuated poliovirus for man. *Am. J. Public Health*, **57**, 1837–1840.

Keswick, B. H., Gerba, C. P., and Goyal, S. M. (1981) Occurrence of enteroviruses in community swimming pools. *Am. J. Public Health*, **71**, 1026–1030.

Khuroo, M. S. (1980) Study of an epidemic of non-A, non-B hepatitis. *Am. J. Med.* **68**, 818–823.

Kogasaka, R., Nakamura, S., Chiba, S., Sakuma, Y., Terashima, H., Yokoyama, T., and Nakao, T. (1981) The 33 to 39 nm viruslike particles, tentatively designated as Sapporo agent associated with an outbreak of acute gastroenteritis. *J. Med. Virol.* **8**, 187–193.

Konno, T., Suzuki, H., Ishida, N., Chiba, R., Mochizuki, K., and Tsunoda, A. (1982) Astrovirus associated epidemic gastroenteritis in Japan. *J. Med. Virol.* **9**, 11–17.

Krikelis, V., Spirou, N., and Serie, C. (1984) Detection of indigenous viruses in raw sewage effluents of the city of Athens, Greece, during a two year survey. International Association of Water Pollution Research Councils, conference, Amsterdam.

Laporte, J., Bobulesco, P., and Rossi, F. (1980) Growth of human and canine enteritic coronavirus in a highly susceptible cell line HRT 18. *C.R. Acad. Sci. (Paris)*, **290**, 623–626.

Le Bris, J. M., Billaudel, S., Bertrand, P., Loukou, G., and Courtieu, A. L. (1983) Recherche des virus et des *Salmonelles* dans la Loire par une methode d'adsorption-elution sur filtres en microfibre de verre. *Tech. Sci. Munic.* **6**, 303–306.

Levin, M. (1978) Fish and shellfish associated disease outbreaks. *J. Water Pollut. Control Fed.* **50**, 1377–1381.

Lippy, C. (1980) Waterborne disease: Occurrence is on the upswing. *J. Am. Waterworks Assoc.* **1**, 57–62.

Lucena, F., Finance, C., Jofre, J., Sancho, J., and Schwartzbrod, L. (1982) Viral pollution determination of superficial waters (river water and seawater) from the urban area of Barcelona (Spain). *Water Res.* **16**, 173–177.

Madeley, C. R., and Cosgrove, B. P. (1976) Caliciviruses in man. *Lancet*, **1**, 199–200.

Madeley, G. R., and Cosgrove, B. P. (1975) 28 nm particles in faeces in infantile gastroenteritis. *Lancet*, **6**, 451–452.

Marques, E., and Martins, M. T. (1983) Enterovirus isolation from seawater from beaches of Baixada Santista. Ninth Latin American Congress for Microbiology, Sao Paulo, Brazil.

Martins, M. T., Soares, L. A., Marques, E., and Molina, A. G. (1983) Human enteric viruses isolated from influents of sewage treatment plants in Sao Paulo, Brazil. *Water Sci.Technol.* **15**, 69–73.

Marzouk, Y., Goyal, S. M., and Gerba, C. P. (1980) Relationship of viruses and indicator bacteria in water and wastewater of Israel. *Water Res.* **14**, 1585–1590.

Matthews, R. E. F. (1982) Classification and nomenclature of viruses. Fourth report of the International Committee of Taxonomy of Viruses. *Intervirology*, **17**, 129–132.

Maurin, J., and Demillac, R. (1981) Application de la methode d'adsorption)elution sur poudre de verre a la mise en evidence des virus hydriques presents dans les rejets de stations d'epuration et dans les eaux superficielles de la region rennaise. *Tech. Sci. Munic.* **81**, 147–150.

Minor, T. E., Allen, C. I., Tsiatis, A. A., Nelson, D. B., and D'Allesio, D. J. (1981) Human infective dose determinations for oral poliovirus type 1 vaccine in infants. *J. Clin. Microbiol.* **13**, 388–389.

Nestor, L., Lazar, L., Sourea, D., and Ionescu, N. (1981) Investigations on viral pollution in the Romanian section of the Danube River during 1972–1977 period. *Zbl. Bakt. Hyg. I. Abt. Orig. B*, **173**, 517–527.

Nestor, I., Costin, L., Sourea, D., and Ionescu, N. (1978) Investigations on the presence of enteroviruses in drinking water. *Rev. Roum. Med. Virol.* **29**, 203–207.

Newaskar, L. D., Vidivans, A. H., and Vaccha, S. M. (1978) Outbreak of viral hepatitis due to water pollution in Pimpri-Chinchwad Township. *Indian J. Environ. Health*, **20**, 79–83.

Notkins, A. L., Yoon, J. W., Onodera, T., Toniolo, A., and Jenson, B. (1981). Virus induced diabetes mellitus. In "Perspectives in Virology," Vol. 11, M. Pollard, Ed. Riss, New York, pp. 141–162.

Payment, P. (1981) Isolation of viruses from drinking water at the Pont-Viau water treatment plant. *Can. J. Microbiol.* **27**, 417–420.

Payment, P., Ayache, R., and Trudel, M. (1983) A survey of enteric viruses in domestic sewage. *Can. J. Microbiol.* **29**, 111–119.

Payment, P., Larose, Y., and Trudel, M. (1979) Poliovirus and other enteroviruses in urban sewage from Laval (Canada): Presence of nonvaccinal strains of poliovirus. *Can. J. Microbiol.* **25**, 1305–1309.

Payne, S. B., Grilli, E. A., and Smith, A. J. (1984) Investigation of an outbreak of adenovirus type 3 infection in a boys' boarding school. *J. Hyg. Camb.* **93**, 277–283.

Prevot, J., Ouvrard, S., Coiron, C., and Festy, B. (1983) Recherche de virus dans les bassins de natation. *Rev. Fr. Sci Eau*, **2**, 73–86.

Provost, P. J., and Hilleman, M. R. (1979) Propagation of human hepatitis A virus in cell culture in vitro. *Proc. Soc. Exp. Biol. Med.* **160**, 213–221.

Rao, V. C., Seidel, K. M., Goyal, S. M., Metcalf, T. G., and Melnick, J .L. (1984) Isolation of enteroviruses from water, suspended solids, and sediments from Galveston Bay: Survival of poliovirus and rotavirus adsorbed to sediments. *Appl. Environ. Microbiol.* **48**, 404–409.

Schiff, G. M., Stefanovic, G. M., Young, E. C., Sander, D. S., Pennekamps, J. K., and Ward, R. L. (1984) Studies of ECHO virus 12 in volunteers: Determination of minimal infectious dose and the effect of previous infection on infectious dose. *J. Infect. Dis.* **150**, 858–866.

Schwartzbrod, L., Finance, C., Aymard, M., Brigaud, M., and Lucena, F. (1985) Recovery of reoviruses from tap water. *Zbl. Bakt. Hyg. I. Abt. Orig. B*, **181**, 383–389.

Schwartzbrod, L., Lucena, F., and Finance, C. (1979) Etude quantitative de la pollution virale dans l'affluent et l'effluent d'une station d'epuration d'eaux residuaires. *J. Fr. Hydrol.* **10**, 7–20.

Simmonds, R. S., Loutit, M. W., and Austin, F. J. (1983) Enteric viruses in New Zealand wastewaters. *N.Z. J. Sci.* **26**, 437–441.

Slade, J. S. (1982) Virus removal by a modern sewage treatment works. In "Viruses and Disinfection of Water and Wastewater," M. Butler et al, Eds. University of Surrey Press, Surrey, U.K.

Smith, E. M., and Gerba, C. P. (1982) Development of a method for detection of human rotavirus in water and sewage. *Appl. Environ. Microbiol.* **43**, 1440–1450.

Sreenivasan, M. A., Sehgal, A., Prasad, S. R., and Dhorje, S. (1984) A seroepidemiologic study of a waterborne epidemic of viral hepatitis in Kolhapur City, India. *J. Hyg.* **93**, 113–122.

Taniguchi, K., Urasawa, S., and Urasawa, T. (1979) Virus-like particles, 35 to 40 nm, associated with an institutional outbreak of acute gastroenteritis in adults. *J. Clin. Microbiol.* **10**, 730–736.

Thornhill, T. S., Wyatt, R. G., Kalica, A. R., Dolin, R., Chanock, R. M., and Kapikian, A. Z. (197) Detection by immune electron microscopy of 26 to 27 nm virus-like particules associated with two family outbreaks of gastroenteritis. *J. Infect. Dis.* **135**, 20–27.

Tyler, J. M. (1982) Viruses in fresh and saline waters. In "Viruses and Disinfection of Water and Wastewater," M. Butler et al, Eds. University of Surrey Press, Surrey, U.K.

Vaucher, Y. F., Ray, C. G., Minnich, L. L., Payne, C. M., Beck, D., and Lowe, P. (1982) Pleomorphic, enveloped, virus-like particles associated with gastrointestinal illness in neonates. *J. Infect. Dis.* **145**, 27–35.

Vilim, V., Pesek, J., Brejcha, O., Zakova, M., Jindr, J., and Pruchova, M. (1977) Viral hepatitis A, water epidemic in a bungalow community. *Cesk. Epidemiol. Mikrobiol. Immunol.* **26**, 46–51.

Viswanathan, R. (1957) Infectious hepatitis in Delhi (1955–1956), a critical study: Epidemiology. *Indian J. Med. Res.* (suppl.) **45**, 1–29.

Ward, R. L., and Akin, E. W. (1984) Minimum infective dose of animal viruses. *C.R.C. Crit. Rev. Environ. Control*, **14**, 297–310.

Wilson, C., Connolly, J. H., and Thomson, D. (1977) Coxsackie B$_2$ virus infection and acute)onset diabetes in a child. *Br. Med. J.* **1**, 1008.

Wong, D. C., Purcell, R. H., Sreenivasan, M. A., Prasad, S. R., and Pavri, K. M. (1980) Epidemic and endemic hepatitis in India: Evidence for a non-A, non-B virus aetiology. *Lancet*, 8200, 876–879.

World Health Organization (1979) Human viruses in water, wastewater and in soil. Scientific Group Report, Technical Reports. World Health Organization, Geneva, 56 pages.

Wyatt, R. G., James, H. D., Pittman, A. L., Hoshino, Y., Greenberg, H. B., Kalica, A. R., Flores, J., and Kapikian, A. Z. (1983) Direct isolation in cell culture of human rotaviruses and their characterization into four serotypes. *J. Clin. Microbiol.* **18**, 310–317.

Chapter 2

GATHERING, MONITORING, AND STORAGE OF SAMPLES

Sampling presents one of the most acute problems in the virological analysis of water systems. There are three major considerations in taking samples. First, the drawing of the samples should be carried out without contamination. Second, the sampling should be representative of the aqueous medium that is to be analyzed. Third, the viruses should not be inactivated during the transportation or the conservation of the samples.

2.1. SAMPLING MATERIAL

2.1.1. Preparation of the Material

Containers for sampling water generally are made of borosilicate glass (1–2 liter vessels) or of plastic that can withstand sterilization (5–25 liter vessels); rarely are these receptacles made of metal. The size of the flasks should be appropriate for the desired volume of the sample; however, for large volumes of water (ie, 100 liters), it is desirable to use several more easily sterilizable 20 or 25 liter jerrycans.

The flasks or vessels that show any cracks should be rejected, and particular attention should be paid to the caps, which are often more fragile. Caps are always more difficult to clean and sterilize due to the many places for microorganisms to hide, such as in the screw threads or under a joint.

The sampling material should be carefully washed and dried before sterilization (except in some cases: See Section 2.1.3.2). New glass material should be treated with an acid solution (5% HCl or 10% HNO_3) or potassium dichromate in a 40 g/liter solution of sulfuric acid. This should be done over 24 hours. After rinsing, the washing is continued by soaking in hot water (50°C) containing a nontoxic detergent; then the inside and outside walls of the flasks are brushed, followed by a long rinsing with tap water, then deionized water, at least 10 times. The drying should be carried out away from any dust.

If the flask is destined for samples of water that have been treated with chlorine, bromine, or ozone, it is advisable to add to the flask a reducing agent such as sodium thiosulfate (1 ml of a 10% sterile solution for samples of 1 liter). If the water to be sampled may contain heavy metals with a concentration higher than 0.01 mg/liter, it is suggested that a chelating agent be added (eg, 3 ml of a 15% sterile solution of EDTA for samples of 1 liter). The caps for the various vessels should be sterilized separately. They are washed, dried, and wrapped individually in Kraft (strong brown) paper. The openings of the vessels are closed off with plugs made of cotton wadding and gauze and covered with Kraft paper or aluminum foil according to the type of sterilization.

2.1.2. Sterilization of the Material

Two types of sterilization are currently applied in the laboratory: humid heat and dry heat.

Sterilization by humid heat is carried out in an autoclave, which permits the treatment of glass or thermoresistant plastic with water vapor under pressure at 121°C for 20 minutes. A complete cycle of sterilization requires a minimum of 85 minutes, that is, 15 minutes for a rise in temperature, 20 minutes for heating at a plateau, and 40 minutes for the lowering of the temperature. The material to be autoclaved should be left open to let the water vapor pass or, better yet, slightly filled with deionized water (around 20 ml per liter of the volume of the vessel, according to Berg et al, 1984)(see Section 2.1.3.2).

Sterilization with dry heat, which is carried out in an oven, is reserved for glass and metals. A sterilization temperature of at least 170°C is applied for 2 hours. A complete cycle of sterilization requires at least 5 hours: 30 minutes for a rise in temperature, 2 hours of heating at a plateau, and 2 and a half hours for the cooling.

The material should be sterilized by batches that have been identified by a code number and contain markers for the verification of the sterilization (cf Section 2.1.3). Furthermore, it is suggested that the material be systematically assigned to the same types of usage; for example, one might separate the flasks used for the sampling of wastewater from those used for sampling potable water.

In very exceptional cases and only for vessels that are destined for sampling wastewater, it is possible to disinfect the flasks with chlorine. For this purpose commercial bleach (theoretically titrating 50 chlorometric degrees) diluted to a tenth serves as a bath in which the flasks can be soaked. After 3 hours the flasks are rinsed with tap water and immersed in a solution of sodium thiosulfate (10 g/liter) to neutralize the residual chlorine. Thorough rinsing with deionized water followed by drying completes the treatment of the vessels.

2.1.3. Verification of the Sterilization

It is absolutely essential to verify the effectiveness of the sterilization equipment and to ensure that each batch of material used in the laboratory has undergone effective treatment.

The sources of error or ineffectiveness during the course of a sterilization treatment are many. Three places for error can be considered as examples

1. The regular pathway for the material in the laboratory has been short circuited and the flasks have not been sterilized.
2. The water vapor inside the autoclave has not been distributed in a homogeneous manner and the sterilization is ineffective (The causes can be a poor purge, the existence of dry air pockets, or the hermetic sealing of perfectly dry flasks.)
3. The time of heating has been much too short for effective sterilization.

Figure 2.1. Self-sticking indicator labels: (*a*) before heating and (*b*) after heating.

2.1.3.1. Verification of the Passage of the Material Through the Sterilization Unit

It is imperative to know the origin of the material and, in particular, to ensure that it really has been to the autoclave or in an oven. Thus it is suggested that the material be identified by means of labels or adhesive tape that contain a substance with a characteristic melting point (121°C for the autoclave or 170°C for the dry heat oven), which blacken and melt when the sterilization temperature is attained (Figure 2.1).

Any flask or piece of equipment that does not have a label with blackened bands should be returned to the sterilization unit. Note, however, that these labels indicate only that there was an exposure at 121°C or at 170°C; nothing can be inferred about the time for sterilization.

2.1.3.2. Verification of the Distribution of the Water Vapor in an Autoclave

Heating at 121°C can offer effective sterilization only in the presence of water vapor. To obtain good sterilization, it is necessary to introduce a small quantity of distilled water into the vessels beforehand (eg, 500 ml per 20 liter can) and not to close them hermetically. As shown in Figure 2.2, a metallic vessel that is perfectly dry and hermetically closed is not really sterilized until it has been heated for 50 minutes.

Furthermore, air pockets can be formed during a poor purge of the autoclave during its start-up. These anomalies can be detected by placing temperature-indicating labels

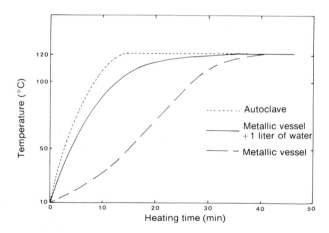

Figure 2.2. Measured temperatures during autoclaving for the outside and inside of a metallic recipient that is dry or filled with water. (Adapted from Lauer and Battles, 1981.)

at different heights in the autoclave (cf Section 2.1.3.1); the labels are protected by gauze pads folded into 40 layers. Correct functioning is revealed by the blackening of the indicator bands placed at strategic positions in the autoclave.

2.1.3.3. *Verification of the Efficiency of Sterilization*

Along with the regular verifications of the sterilization equipment (every 250 cycles or every 6 months) such as the timing mechanisms and temperature recorders, it is advisable to add a continuous control of the sterilization cycle and of its effectiveness. This control should apply directly to the vessels and indicators.

When batches of flasks are sterilized, 10% of them should be checked. After selecting six flasks at random, add to three of them 10 ml of sterilized trypticase soy broth (indicating aerobic bacteria and yeast) and to the remaining three 10 ml of resazurine thioglycolate broth (indicating anaerobic bacteria). Stopper the flasks, stir them to wash the inside walls and the cap, and incubate at 37°C for 5 to 10 days. Any microbial development indicates that the sterilization has been ineffective.

The control with the aid of indicators is either physicochemical (Brown tubes) or bacteriological (tubes containing the spores of *Bacillus stearothermophilus* and a tube of growth medium). These tubes, surrounded by gauze, are placed in the middle of the batch of material to be sterilized.

a. Physicochemical Control. The Brown tubes contain chemical substances which, at a given temperature and for a determined period of time, demonstrate good sterilization by a thermochemical reaction that produces a characteristically colored substance.

b. Bacteriological Control. After sterilization, the vials of culture medium incorporated into a tube containing the spores of *B. stearothermophilus* are broken. If all the spores have not been killed by the sterilization, the survivors will be able to develop. After 48 hours of incubation at 56°C, the appearance of a yellow color in the middle of the culture (originally violet) indicates bacterial development and consequently the lack of sterilization.

To set up a control for effective sterilization, the laboratory should be equipped with a sufficient reserve of material such that sterilization proceeds only when the bacterial samples have tested negative.

2.2. CONTROL OF THE SAMPLING PERSONNEL AND TECHNICIANS

The person doing the sampling as well as all the technicians who will participate in the virological analysis of the sample can be asymptomatic carriers of viruses. They thus represent an important potential source of contamination. Even though the phenomenon is well known in bacteriology, it seems to have been underestimated in virology. Since 1976 numerous polemics have arisen in the United States concerning the isolation of enteroviruses from the public distribution of water, and the results have been hotly contested because of the absence of verification or control of the sampling personnel and of the technicians. Also, Akin and Jakubowski (1976) have proposed that during analyses of water in distribution systems or swimming pools, it be made certain that the personnel are not carriers of viruses. The systematic analysis of samples from the throat and fecal matter of the personnel who are in any way connected with the work remains the simplest method. Such a procedure is certainly costly, but it permits one to answer any criticisms and to justify the results with a maximum of security.

2.3. SAMPLING DESIGN FOR MONITORING WATERS

The viral populations in aquatic environments present both spatial and temporal variability. The results of any virological analysis conducted without knowing about such variability, as well as the heterogeneity of the distribution of the viruses in water media, will be noninterpretable and useless. However, no general rule has yet been proposed to evaluate sampling programs for the monitoring of the virological quality of water systems. Also, it is necessary for each laboratory to define an integrated strategy for sampling which incorporates such parameters as the volume, frequency, place, and date of the sampling.

It is obvious that a large number of analyses should be carried out to afford the most precise result possible. All the same, as in the bacteriology of water systems, an effort should be made to gather the maximum number of samples in the field rather than to repeat diverse titrations on subsamples (Maul and Block, 1983).

Furthermore, knowledge of the distribution of viral particles in water systems permits one to design the sampling procedures for a monitoring program. Based on the results obtained in bacteriology, it is clear that the model of a Poisson distribution (random distribution) is not suited for the description of the distribution of viral populations in water.

The negative binomial law, which represents a generalization of the Poisson distribution and of the log–normal law, appears to be much more suitable for this situation (Maul and El Shaarawi, 1985). Also, it does not need a logarithmic transformation of the values.

The negative binomial distribution is defined by equation 2-1:

$$P(X = R) = \frac{(k + r - 1)!}{r! - (k - 1)!} \frac{p^r}{(1 + p)^{k+r}} \tag{2-1}$$

where the distribution is specified by the parameters p and k. The mean λ of the distribution is equal to the product of pk and of a variance given by the formula $\sigma^2 = p(1 + p)k$. A true program of sampling should be made up either from previous results or from a systematic study. The set of results that is adjusted to the law of probabilities will permit one to approximate the values of k and p, then to calculate the minimum number of samples for new analyses. The parameter k and the viral density having been approximated, the minimum number of samples for new series of analyses can be calculated. The example in Figure 2.3 shows that the smaller the values of k (a very heterogeneous environment), the larger the number of samples to be taken. This value can reach 50 to 60 per zone studied and per series of samples. Under these conditions, a study designed correctly will prove to be extremely costly. On the contrary, the greater the value of k (a tendency toward homogeneity; Poisson distribution), the smaller the number of samples to be taken.

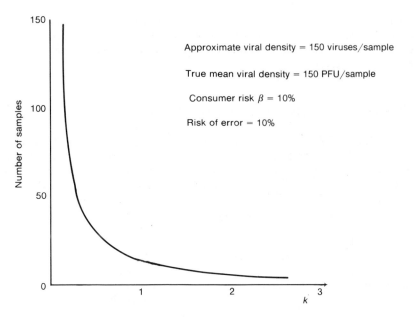

Figure 2.3. Number of samples as a function of the value of k.

2.3.1. Sampling of Wastewater

Urban wastewater represents the material that is richest in enteric viruses. Raw wastewater can be analyzed either by direct inoculation or after concentration, whereas treated wastewater must be concentrated. Thus sample volume ranges from several milliliters to 50 liters.

The heterogeneity at one point in the urban environment is smaller than that for river water, and consecutive samples (every minute) give rather similar results. Nevertheless, large variations in the viral concentrations can be observed during the course of a year (Hejkal et al, 1984) and even during the course of one day (Hugues et al, 1982; Schwartzbrod et al, 1985). Such variations are characteristic of the site and depend particularly on the socioeconomic level of the population, on the amount of rain, on the length of the wastewater collecting network, and on the day of the sampling (Rolland et al, 1983a). Figure 2.4 gives an example of such variations, which are well correlated with the bacterial indicators of fecal pollution in the raw wastewater.

Since variations with a factor of 5 to 10 can be observed during the course of a day, any sampling that is done without knowledge of the flow does not allow a correct quantitative evaluation. An automatic composite sampling, which is adapted to the flow of the effluents, gives a good picture of the flow of viruses in urban wastewater (Rolland et al, 1982).

2.3.2. Sampling of River Water

The guidelines of the European Community Commissions (Commissions des Communautes Europeennes, 1975) recommend that 10 liters of water be used for the

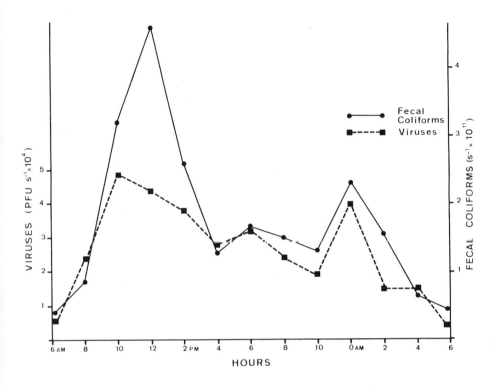

Figure 2.4. Flow of physicochemical and microbiological pollutants in raw wastewater. (Adapted from Rolland et al, 1983b.)

analysis of swimming water, without any specification for the frequency of sampling. However, larger samples (20–100 liters) should be taken for investigations of the impact of wastewater effluent on a river and its diffusion. It is advisable to avoid sampling in zones without much flow and also too close to the river banks (except in the case of swimming zones), where the so-called bank effect interferes with the dispersion of suspended matter and microorganisms.

The samples should be taken at 30 cm below the surface of the water—that is, in a zone that is deep enough to ensure that the sampling does not disturb any sediments, which are usually richer in microorganisms than the circulating water. The number of samples to be taken at one point of the river and at the same moment depends uniquely on the heterogeneity of the system sampled. Very often consecutive samples at one point (at 1 minute intervals) will show extremely large differences in viral concentration (Table 2.1).

If one adds the very large variations over time, as have been observed with the total number of coliform bacteria in the Moselle River (Figure 2.5), a quantitative estimate of the viral flux in a river is still possible but very costly and complicated (involving number of samples taken, positioning of the sampling in three dimensions, etc).

Table 2.1. Viral concentrations of six samplings of river water
taken at 1 minute intervals

Sampling number	Viral concentration (PFU/liter)
1	0
2	0
3	210
4	0
5	22
6	283

Source: Adapted from Foliguet et al, (1973).

Given this enormous heterogeneity of water systems, any quality monitoring of surface water remains extremely difficult. For any sampling design of this nature, two erroneous decisions are possible: the first is to declare that the quality of the water violates regulations when really it does not; the second is to declare compliance with regulations when, in fact, this is not true.

2.3.3. Sampling of Potable Water

By definition, potable water should contain no viral particles or, at least, an extremely small number. Also, the virological analysis should be conducted on samples containing at least 100 to 1000 liters of water.

Moreover, the proper frequency for sampling potable water is difficult to determine. A program designed for water quality monitoring should, within a small risk of error and from a given number of samples, assure that the water is free of viral contamination. However, it is clear that given the low viral density of water intended for drinking, such an operation will require the analysis of a large number of samples for any given period of analysis (a day or a week) and for a particular point of the

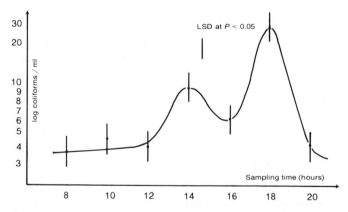

Figure 2.5. Variation of the bacterial concentrations in the water of the Moselle River recorded during the course of one day, July 16, 1981. LSD, Least significant difference. (From Maul et al, 1982.)

network. Thus, with the most optimistic of hypotheses—namely, a viral distribution that is described by a Poisson distribution in a given zone, a viral density in the neighborhood of 0.1 virus/1000 liters, and a concentration method with a 100% yield (!)—it might be necessary to analyze at least 10 samples of 1000 liters per zone.

This number, when multiplied by the number of zones to be studied, can appear rather large, but one must recall that the bacteriological controls of potable water are just as large (a minimum of 170 samples per month for a city of 300,000 inhabitants, according to Bordner et al, 1978). In addition, since a network can be considered to be a collection of subsystems (Maul et al, 1985) in which the populations of microorganisms are described by a negative binomial distribution, the number of samples might even increase. Furthermore, the quantitative virological monitoring of potable water does not make sense.

2.4. STORAGE OF SAMPLES

Virological analysis has a chance of being truly representative only if it is carried out immediately after the samples have been taken. The conservation of the samples of water in the laboratory, even at 4°C, should remain an exceptional case. Losses of 10 to 90% of the viral populations have been demonstrated after a period of conservation varying from 2 to 48 hours (Rao et al, 1977; Vilagines, 1982). This apparent decrease in the viral titer can result from the phenomena of aggregation and adsorption or from biological inactivation.

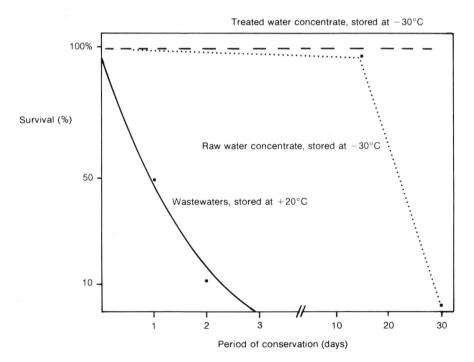

Figure 2.6. Survival of Sabin type I poliomyelitic virus in wastewater and in concentrates. (From Vilagines, 1982.)

As shown in Figure 2.6, only the concentrates of the samples can be conserved, after decontamination, either several days at 4°C or several weeks at − 30°C.

REFERENCES

Akin, E. W., and Jakubowski, W. (1976) Viruses in finished water: The Occoquan experience. Proceedings of the AWWA Conference on Water Quality Technology, San Diego, CA, pp. 110.

Berg, G., Safferman, R. S., Dahling, D. R., Berman, D., and Hurst, C. Y. (1984) "U.S. Environmental Protection Agency Manual of Methods for Virology." U.S. EPA Publication EPA-600/14-84-013, Cincinnati, OH.

Bordner R., Winter, J., and Scarpino, P. (1978) Microbiological methods for monitoring the environment: Water and wastes. U.S. Environmental Protection Agency, EPA, Cincinnati, OH, Report EPA-600/18-76-017. 354 pp.

Commissions des Communautes Europeennes (December 1975) Directive: Qualité requise des eaux destinees a la baignade. *J. Offi. Communautes Euro.*

Foliguet, J. M., Block, J. C., Hartemann, P., and Joret, J. C. (1978) Recent developments of virological research in France. In "Abstracts of the Fourth International Congress for Virology." The Hague.

Hejkal, T. W., Smith, E. M., and Gerba, C. P. (1984) Seasonal occurrence of *Rotavirus* in sewage. *Appl. Environ. Microbiol.* **47**, 588–590.

Hugues, B., Vidal, H., Andre, M., Plissier, M., Bouron, J., Lefevre, J. R., and Cini, A. (1982) Détermination sur 24 heures des flux bactériens et viraux entrant et sortant de la station de traitement de niveau B de Cannes. *Sci l'Eau,* **1**, 151–162.

Lauer, J. L., and Battles, D. R. (1981) Infections laboratory waste: Decontamination by autoclaving. Presented to the 81st Annual Meeting of the American Society for Microbiology (ASM), Dallas.

Maul, A., and Block, J. C. (1983) Microplate fecal coliform method to monitor stream water pollution. *Appl. Environ. Microbiol.* **46**, 1032–1037.

Maul, A., Dollard, M. A., and Block, J. C. (1982) Etude de l'hétérogénéité spatio-temporelle des bactéries coliformes en rivière. *J. Fr. Hydrol.* **13**, 141–156.

Maul, A., and El Shaarawi, A. H. (1985) Stratégie de prelevement in, *Bacteriologie des Milieux Aquatiques: Aspects Écologiques et Sanitaires*, G. Martin, Ed. Lavoisier, Paris.

Maul, A., El Shaarawi, A. H., and Block, J. C. (1985) Heterotrophic bacteria in water distribution systems. I. Spatial and temporal variations. *Sci. Total Environ.* **44**, 201–214.

Ministers Français de la Santé (1976) Surveillance sanitaire des baignades en mer. Circular (June 23).

Rao, V. C., Lakhe, S. B., Waghmare, S. V., and Dube, P. (1977) Virus removal in activated sludge sewage treatment. *Prog. Water Technol.* **9**, 113–127.

Rolland, D., Joret, J. C., Mary, S. and Schwartzbrod, L. (1982) Stratégie de prélèvement pour l'analyse virologique des eaux usées. *J. Fr. Hydrol.* **13**, 93–104.

Rolland, D., Hartemann, P., Joret, J. C., Hassen, A., and Foliguet, J. M. (1983a) Evaluation of the load of enteroviruses in a biological wastewater treatment plant. *Water Sci. Technol.* **15**, 115–121.

Rolland, D., Joret, J. C., Villeval, F., Block, J. C., Hartemann, P., and Foliguet, J. M. (1983b) Sampling strategy for detecting viruses in a sewage treatment plant. *Appl. Environ. Microbiol.* **45**, 1767–1774.

Schwartzbrod, L., Vilagines, P. H., Schwartzbrod, J., Sarrette, B., Vilagines, R., and Collomb, J. (1985) Evaluation of the viral population in two wastewater treatment plants: Study of different sampling techniques. *Water Res.* **19**, 1353–1356.

Vilagines, R. (1982) Etude de la fluctuation des populations virales avant et après traitement biologique des eaux usees. Final report, no 81-033, to the French Ministry of the Environment, Paris.

Chapter 3

CONCENTRATION METHODS

Except in the case of raw, urban wastewater, the viral concentrations appearing in waters to be analyzed are too low to permit the samples to be directly inoculated into susceptible systems. A concentration step for the virus particles is necessary to bring the sample volume of several liters down to a few milliliters. A good method of concentration should fulfill several criteria: it should be technically easy to accomplish within a short time, have a high recovery yield (of the virus), treat a large range of viruses, give a small volume of concentrate, and not to be costly.

All of the extremely numerous concentration methods proposed in the literature (Foliguet et al, 1973; Belfort and Dziewulski, 1982; Gerba, 1984) profit from certain of the physical and chemical characteristics of viral particles, particularly their charge, size, and mass. These characteristics permit the definition of three large groups of concentration methods: adsorption, filtration, and centrifugation.

Viruses are biocolloids sized from 10 to 300 nm, negatively charged at the pH of natural waters, and capable of being adsorbed in monolayers on solid surfaces. This phenomenon fits a Langmuir or a Freundlich type of isotherm. The interaction between the viral particle surrounded by a layer of both ions and water molecules (mobile Gouy–Chapmann layer), and the adsorption surface can be approximated by the model described by the Derjaguin–Landau–Verwey–Overbeek (DLVO) theory of stable colloids. Even so, Shields and Farrah (1983) have shown that in certain cases, hydrophobic interactions may play a more important role than electrostatic interactions.

Knowledge of these interactions determines the choice of the type of adsorbent to be utilized for concentrating the viruses (specific surface, charge), the type of adsorption adjuvant (trivalent ions), and the type of elution liquid (organic solution, detergent, antichaotropic saline solution, etc). Each concentration method presents specific advantages and inconveniences. These are summarized in Table 3.1.

Two different methods have been chosen from experiments in the laboratory and in the field and are presented in the sections that follow.

1. The gauze pad method.
2. The methods of virus adsorption on supports followed by elution. In practice, four types of support are usable:
   a. Cellulose nitrate membranes (Cliver, 1967)
   b. Glass microfiber filter cartridges (Sobsey et al, 1973)
   c. Powdered glass (Sarrette et al, 1977)
   d. Positively charged filters (Sobsey and Glass, 1980).

Table 3.1. Summary of applications and limitations of concentration methods of waterborne viruses
(from Belfort and Dziewulski, 1982)

Method	Initial Volume of Water	Quality of Water	Concentration of Virus in Water	Suggested Application	Limitations or Disadvantages
1. Filter adsorption-elution procedures	large	Low concentration of competitive adsorbers present	low	Reclaimed wastewater and finished waters	Additional development needed for application to wastewaters and polluted natural waters
2. Precipitation by or adsorption to various charged species	small	High organics concentration acceptable	high	Raw or partially treated sewage	Yet to be shown efficient with large volumes at low virus concentration
3. Polymer two-phase separation	small	High organics concentration acceptable	high	Sewage, treated effluents and other raw materials	Processing is slow and virus recovery is inaccurate and of low precision
4. Membrane filtration methods a. ultrafiltration					
1. soluble filters	small	Good	—	Clean waters	Poor performance with unclarified effluents
2. tangential flow	large	Unknown	low	Treated effluents and finished waters	Looks promising but needs additional testing with waste and polluted waters

Method					
b. reverse osmosis (hyperfiltration)	small	Unknown	low	Treated effluents and finished waters	Also concentrates cytotoxic compounds which adversely affect assay methods
c. hydroextraction	small	High organics	large	Raw and treated sewage	High virus loss with wastewaters
d. electro-osmosis	small	Low concentration pressure	low	Clear waters	Equipment expensive and not portable
5. Other methods					
a. ultra-centifuge	small	Good	high	Clean waters	Equipment expensive but not portable
b. electrophoresis	small	Unknown	high	Clean waters	Equipment expensive but not portable
c. freeze concentration	small	Good	high	Clean waters	Not practical yet
d. gauze pad	large	Unknown	unknown	Treated waters	Not quantiative or reproducible
e. vegetable floc	small	Good	high	Clean waters	Not tested extensively
f. affinity chromatography	small	Good	high	Clean waters	Not tested extensively

Three types of liquid are currently employed for elution:

3% beef extract solution at pH 9.5

0.05 M glycine–NaOH solution at pH 9.5 or 11.5

Glycine and beef extract solution

(0.3% beef extract solution prepared in a solution of 0.05 M glycine and NaOH at pH 9.5.)

Finally, we will look at the secondary concentration methods currently applied to the elution liquids obtained by the preceding methods.

3.1. THE GAUZE PAD METHOD

The gauze pad method utilizes a property of hydrophilic gauze that has been traversed by a current of water, namely, the capacity to retain suspended materials such as clay, organic colloids, algae, bacteria, and the viruses present in that water. This retention capability is put to use by immersing pads of hydrophilic gauze in a current of the water that is to be analyzed.

3.1.1. Preparation of the Gauze Pads

The gauze pads are prepared, as shown in Figure 3.1, from a five-layer piece of gauze (3 m × 3 m), which is folded to present a rectangle, *ABCD*, 100 cm by 30 cm. All along length *DC* there are bands 3 to 4 cm wide cut out up to 5 cm from line *AB*. Then, a string is knotted at the upper limit of the bands, making a sort of plug. The string is left long enough (30 cm) to be used for tieing later. To increase the plug's effectiveness as a filter, it is necessary to separate the bands of gauze, one by one. This considerably increases the volume and, above all, the surface of the gauze in contact

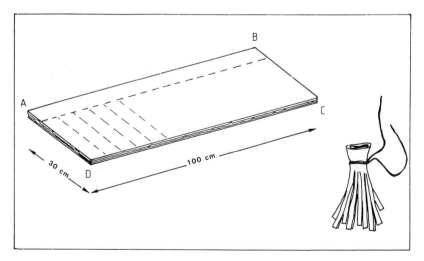

Figure 3.1. Preparation of gauze pads.

with the water. The plug is then wrapped in paper (first an envelope of filter paper, then Kraft paper) and sterilized for 20 minutes at 121°C in an autoclave.

3.1.2. Positioning of the Gauze Pads

Handled aseptically, the pads are weighted down with enough ballast to ensure that they will be submerged to a depth of around 30 cm when put into the current of water to be analyzed. They are tied either to floats that remain on the surface of the river or to hooks attached to the sides of sewers. The pads are left in place for 24 hours.

3.1.3. Recovery of the Pads and Water

The pads are taken out without draining or wringing and immediately put into a sterile jar to permit the collection of the water that has been soaked up. They are rapidly transported at low temperature ($+4-+6°C$) to the laboratory.

The water retained in the gauze is then wrung out by simple hand torsion of the plug (sterile gloves!), and the water is collected in a jar. The volume varies from 100 to 600 ml, which necessitates a secondary concentration of this liquid if the viral concentration is assumed to be too low (cf Section 3.3).

3.1.4. Limitations of the Method

The gauze pad method is extremely simple and economical but it does not give quantitative results. Of course, the volume of water filtered through the pad is not measurable, and the effectiveness of the filtering system unknown (the concentration factor is estimated to be between 1 and 100). Furthermore, this method cannot be used for clear waters that are low in suspended matter (Fattal and Katzenelson, 1976) but is reserved for waste and surface waters.

3.2. ADSORPTION–ELUTION METHODS

The methods of adsorption–elution accommodate filtration either through a series of membrane or cartridge filters or through so-called dynamic filters (powdered glass).

3.2.1. Cellulose Ester Filters

Cellulose ester filters are flat membranes with a porosity greater than the size of viruses; the viruses, however, are retained by an adsorption phenomenon.

3.2.1.1. Filtration Material

The membranes utilized have a porosity of 0.45 μm (Millipore HA or equivalent) and they are connected with two prefilters made of glass fiber (Millipore AP_{20} and AP_{15} or equivalent). Four diameters of filters and prefilters can be chosen (47, 90, 142, or 293 mm), as a function of the volume of water to be analyzed.

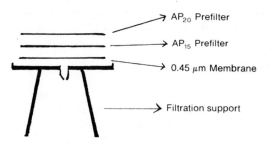

Figure 3.2. The arrangement of filtration materials.

These filters are arranged on filter holders, starting with the 0.45 μm membrane and ending with the AP_{20} prefilter (Fig. 3.2).

Before using, the filtration material is sterilized in an autoclave at 121°C for 20 minutes.

3.2.1.2. Preparation of the Samples

To facilitate the adsorption of the viruses on the membrane during the filtration step, the samples are first complemented with some 1 M $MgCl_2$ solution to obtain a final concentration of 0.05 M, then acidified to pH 3.5 with the aid of a 1 M HCl solution, stirring constantly (Berg et al, 1984).

3.2.1.3. Operations

The samples are filtered under positive pressure, pushing the liquid through the filter, with the aid of a pump or of a compressed gas (eg, nitrogen).

After filtration, the viral particles are eluted with a buffered 3% solution of beef extract at pH 9. After preliminary contact of 30 minutes, the eluant solution passes through the prefilters and filter under positive pressure. The eluate that is obtained, whose volume varies according to the diameter of the filters used, is then neutralized to pH 7.2. It can be used directly after decontamination for the inoculation of sensitive systems, or it can undergo a secondary concentration before analysis (cf Section 3.3).

3.2.1.4. Limitations of the Method

The method is relatively efficient insofar as it permits 60% recuperation (Beytout et al, 1977), but the low porosity of the membranes limits its use to clear water samples or to volumes of 10 liters or less for surface waters.

3.2.2. Glass Microfiber Filters

Glass fiber filters are made up of glass microfibers bound by an epoxy resin. They are negatively charged, which permits enteroviruses to be adsorbed at a pH lower than their isoelectric point (Sobsey et al, 1973).

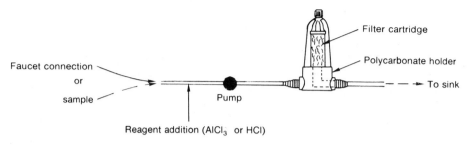

Figure 3.3. Glass microfiber filtration system.

3.2.2.1. Filtration Material

The filters are cartridges 60 mm high, which are sterilizable in autoclaves. Different filters can be used, including the Cox, Filterite, Cartridge, or Balston C100-12 (8 μm filtration grade) models. They are placed on a support composed of a polycarbonate holder that can be sterilized in an autoclave. Each entrance of the support is hooked up to a sterilizable rubber tube (Fig. 3.3). Following the direction of filtration indicated on the polycarbonate holder, one of the tubes is connected to one end, either to the evacuation end or to a pump that has been sterilized previously (by passing a 10 g/liter chlorine solution followed by neutralization with a sterile solution of sodium thiosulfate).

3.2.2.2. Preparation of the Water Samples

The water is brought to a pH of 3.5 by addition of hydrochloric acid. The acid must be added with constant mixing to avoid large localized acidification effects. Adding aluminum chloride to obtain a final concentration of 5×10^{-4} M aids in the adsorption of the virions.

3.2.2.3. Operations

Water samples can be filtered through glass microfiber cartridges either under pressure or by aspiration at a rate of 100 to 150 liters/hour. After filtration of the whole sample, the viruses are eluted from the support by circulating a 3% beef extract solution at pH 9.5. Taking into consideration the thickness of the tubes and the type of pump used, around 300 ml of the elution liquid is necessary and should circulate through the filter for 2 minutes. After elution, the beef extract solution is recovered and neutralized, and should undergo a secondary concentration (cf Section 3.3).

To avoid this secondary concentration step, however, the filters can be eluted according to another procedure. After adsorption of the virus, it is advisable to take the filters aseptically from the polycarbonate holder and cut them into pieces approximately 1 cm square. The pieces are ground for 5 minutes in a blender at 20,000 rpm in 30 ml of a 3% beef extract solution at pH 9.5, avoiding heating all the while. The mixture obtained is filtered through sterile gauze and the filtration liquid is centrifuged at 10,000 g for 5 minutes. The top layer is then neutralized to pH 7.2 and decontaminated (cf Section 3.4).

3.2.2.4. Limitations of the Method

The method for enterovirus concentration on glass microfiber filters gives a poor yield on the average with wastewater but near 70% with river water or with water systems experimentally contaminated with type 1 poliomyelitic virus.

The technique is easily applicable to the three categories of water (potable water, surface waters, and wastewaters), but the volume passed through each filter must be limited to avoid clogging. Around 100, 20, and 5 liters, respectively, of the three types of water can be filtered through cartridges 60 mm high

The method presents the advantage of requiring material that is only slightly fragile, and it is well adapted to field analyses. Furthermore, it has been demonstrated that for concentrations taken far from the laboratory, the filters can be transported by mail after immersion in a 3% solution of beef extract at pH 7 containing antibiotics (10,000 units of penicillin and 10 mg of streptomycin per milliliter) (Joret and Block, 1981), and if possible at a temperature of $+4°C$ (Dahling and Wright, 1984).

3.2.3. Filtration On Powdered Glass

The powder from borosilicate pyrex glass that has been ground into 100 to 200 μm particles and is negatively charged represents an excellent adsorbent for enteroviruses at a pH lower than their isoelectric point (Sarrette et al, 1977). Concentration is carried out by filtration of water samples through a powdered glass fluidized bed.

3.2.3.1. Filtration Material

The apparatus proposed by Schwartzbrod and Lucena-Gutierrez (1978) is composed of two elements. Element 1 (Fig. 3.4) is formed by a column of Pyrex glass (50 mm × 340 mm) with a spherical expansion chamber on the upper part (180 mm in diameter), along with a side arm (1) for water evacuation. The column has two lateral tubes (2 and 3), and its lower extremity (4) is connected to element 2 by means of a flexible rubber joint. Element 2 (Fig. 3.5) is composed of Pyrex tubing comprising at its upper part a stricture for supporting a cotton wad. It also consists of two stopcocks (A and B) and a lateral side arm (5). By its lower part, it is connected to a 125 ml flask provided with a twoholed stopper.

The powdered glass is introduced into element 1. The glass tubing is equipped with rubber tubes, which are plugged at the extremities by cotton wads. The assembled apparatus is sterilized in an autoclave at 121°C for 20 minutes.

3.2.3.2. Preparation of the Water Samples

As in the case of filtration by glass microfiber filters and observing the same precautions, the sample of water is acidified to pH 3.5 and aluminum chloride is added to obtain a final concentration of 5×10^{-4} M.

3.2.3.3. Operations

The sterile assembled filtration system is connected to the reservoir of water to be analyzed and to a vacuum tube (Fig. 3.6). The apparatus also can be arranged in such a

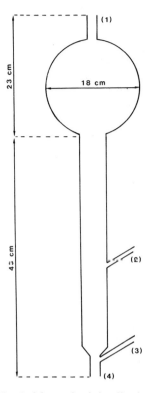

Figure 3.4. Part 1 of the powdered glass filtration apparatus.

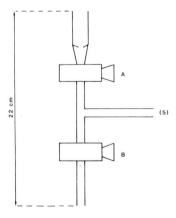

Figure 3.5. Part 2 of the powdered glass filtration apparatus.

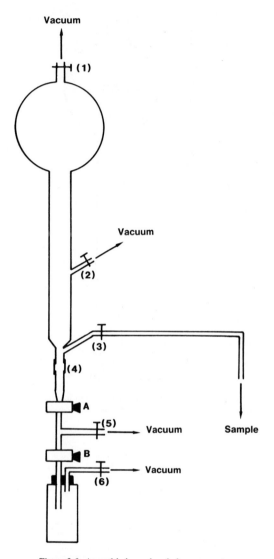

Figure 3.6. Assembled powdered glass apparatus.

way as to work under positive pressure. The steps are as follows.

1. Tube 3 is connected to the sample to be analyzed. Tubes 1, 2, 5, and 6 are connected with the source of vacuum and are also clamped.
2. With tubes 1 and 3 open, the water is aspirated into the apparatus, carrying along with it the powdered glass, which is rapidly put into suspension forming a fluidizedbed filter that extends over the whole height of the column and up to the lower third of the expansion chamber. A filtration rate of 60 liters per hour is advisable.

3. When the whole sample of water has been filtered through the powdered glass, tube 3 is rapidly closed, avoiding any aspiration of air. Tube 1 is opened to the atmosphere, then tubes 4 and 5 and stopcock A are opened. The powder decants into the base of the column.

4. The water on top is then eliminated, first by tube 2 and then by tube 5. When the level of water arrives at 0.5 cm above the powdered glass, 150 ml of the 3% beef extract solution at pH 9.5 is introduced by tube 1.

5. When the elution liquid's front reaches the lower part of the column, tube 5 is closed and stopcock B is opened, which then directs the elution liquid into the flask, which is itself connected to a vacuum by tube 6. Only the first 30 ml is collected, neutralized to pH 7.2, and decontaminated (cf Section 3.4) for submission to virological analysis.

3.2.3.4. Limitations of the Method

The filtration is not limited by the volume of the sample even in the case of waters loaded with suspended matter because the fluidized bed, by definition, cannot be clogged. However, the yield for the method varies with the type of water analyzed: from 60% with potable water, it falls abruptly to 20% with urban wastewater, corresponding to the yield for the glass microfiber technique (Joret et al, 1980).

For sample volumes less than 100 liters, the powdered glass method has the advantage of giving an elution liquid with a small volume (30 ml), all of which can be inoculated into cell cultures without the need for a secondary concentration step.

For samples larger than 100 liters, a new apparatus has been proposed by Vilagines et al (1979) and Vilagines (1980), necessitating, however, a secondary concentration of the elution liquid.

3.2.4. Positively Charged Filters

Positively charged filters are made of cellulose and modified exchange resin for anions.

3.2.4.1. Filtration Material

The filters are either in the form of a cartridge or of disks that are sterilizable in an autoclave. Different filters can be used (eg, Virozorb, 1 MDS^x, Zeta-Plus 60 S Filter^x). The Virozorb filter is a tube 25 cm long, which develops a large surface for filtration. This cartridge is put into a holder that can be sterilized in an autoclave.

3.2.4.2. Preparation of the Water Samples

One of the advantages of positively charged filters is that they need neither acidification nor addition of salts to the samples of water. However, it has been demonstrated that despite the excellent effectiveness of adsorption (Sobsey and Glass, 1980) for the range of pH between 3.5 and 7.5, the adsorption decreases considerably for pH values greater than 7.5. Thus the systematic verification of the pH of the water to be analyzed is recommended, so that if necessary, one may bring it back to around neutrality (Melnick et al, 1984) or even to pH 6 (Guttman-Bass et al, 1985).

3.2.4.3. Operations

The samples of water are filtered through Virozorb filters under positive pressure at the speed of 2 ml per minute per square centimeter of filter surface. When the entire sample has been filtered, the water remaining at the level of the filtering cartridge is pushed out by compressed air. The adsorbed viruses are then eluted by circulating 1600 ml of a glycine–0.3% beef extract solution or 3% pH 9.5 beef extract solution through the filter for 5 minutes. At the end of elution the solution is immediately neutralized to pH 7.2 and is submitted to a secondary concentration.

3.2.4.4. Limitations of the Method

The concentration method of enteroviruses on positively charged filters has been tested mostly with drinking water. In this case, it allows the filtration of 1000 liter samples of with an adsorption yield higher than 80% and a rate of recovery of viruses of about 60%.

This technique does not use any fragile material, and it presents the advantage of needing only a simple adjustment of the pH to neutrality for waters that are too alkaline. Furthermore, Keswick (1983) has shown that type 1 polioviruses and SA 11 rotaviruses adsorbed on electropositive filters survive at least 5 weeks at +4°C. However, the filters that are now used are relatively costly.

3.3. SECONDARY CONCENTRATION METHODS

The elution liquids collected after the water samples have been concentrated are usually of a volume that is too large to be inoculated into sensitive cell cultures. It is necessary then to proceed with a secondary concentration, which can be carried out by one of several methods.

3.3.1. Secondary Concentration by Organic Flocculation

The methods of organic coagulationflocculation rely on the property that proteins in solution coagulate at an acid pH lower than their isoelectric point. In the course of the formation of the protein flocs, the viruses of the sample are adsorbed or embedded. One simply recovers the flocs and dissolves them in a low-volume buffer solution to obtain a concentrated viral suspension.

Two groups of proteins are utilized for flocculations: beef extract (Katzenelson et al, 1976) and casein (Bitton et al, 1979).

3.3.1.1. Flocculation by a Solution of Beef Extract

The solutions of beef extract that are used for flocculation come either from elution of the filters used in the preceding methods or from samples of water (squeezed out of gauze pads, surface water, etc) complemented with 3% beef extract.

The beef extract solutions are brought to pH 3.5 by addition of hydrochloric acid under constant stirring, which is continued for 30 minutes to help the flocculation. The flocs are recovered by centrifuged at 3000 g for 10 minutes. The resulting pellet is dissolved in a sterile buffer solution of sodium hydrogen phosphate (0.15 M), pH 7.2, in the ratio of 5 ml of phosphate buffer to 100 ml of flocculated beef extract solution. The dissolving of the flocs is sometimes slow, and it is advisable in certain cases to stir the pellet for 5 to 10 minutes. The resulting solution is decontaminated before virological analysis (cf Section 3.4).

It is necessary to point out a certain heterogeneity in the quality of commercial beef extracts. Some batches do not permit satisfactory flocculation, and it is thus essential to test each batch of beef extract before beginning an experiment (Hurst et al, 1984) or to add a flocculation aid (Payment et al, 1984).

3.3.1.2. Flocculation by Casein Solution

Nonfat powdered milk or isoelectric casein is added to the sample to be analyzed for a final concentration of 500 mg/liter. After complete solution, the sample is brought to pH 4.3 by addition of normal hydrochloric acid (ie, slightly below the isoelectric point of casein). Flocculation is helped by gentle stirring for 30 minutes. The resulting precipitate is centrifuged at 10,000 g for 10 minutes and then dissolved in 2 ml of a pH 9.5 sodium hydrogen phosphate solution (0.15 M) for every 100 ml of previously flocculated casein solution. After dissolving, the pH is adjusted to 7–7.2 and the solution decontaminated (cf Section 3.4) before being submitted to virological analysis.

3.3.1.3. Limitations of the Flocculation Methods

The flocculation methods are extremely easy to employ and appear to be good methods for secondary concentration of eluates smaller than 2 or 3 liters. The average yield of viral recovery is about 70%.

3.3.2. Secondary Concentration with Aluminum Hydroxide Followed by Hydroextraction

3.3.2.1. Principles

The use of aluminum hydroxide for secondary concentration, followed by hydroextraction was first proposed by Wallis and Melnick (1967), then taken up by different teams (Farrah et al, 1976; Melnick et al, 1984). In the liquid containing the viruses, one forms a fine precipitate of aluminum hydroxide on which the viral particles are adsorbed. The viruses that are thus attached to the flocs are then eluted by an alkaline protein solution. This is once more concentrated by a simple procedure of hydroextraction with a dialysis tube.

3.3.2.2. Operations

The neutralized elution liquid (eg, a solution of glycine) is prepared in such a way that it contains 0.003 M $AlCl_3$. Then the pH is adjusted to 7 with a solution of 1 M sodium carbonate. After gentle magnetic stirring for 5 minutes, the flocs are formed and left to sediment for 30 minutes. Most of the liquid on top is then eliminated and the remaining mixture is centrifuged at 1000 g for 3 minutes.

The viruses that are present in the liquid will be adsorbed on the flocs; their elution is brought about by mixing the flocs with 3 volumes of a 1 M glycine solution in fetal calf serum (pH 11.5). After magnetic stirring, the mixture is centrifuged, and the liquid above is taken off and neutralized by the addition of a 1 M solution of glycine (pH 2).

From this elution liquid one proceeds to a hydroextraction. The elution liquid is poured into a dialysis tube, which is closed and covered with 20,000-weight polyethylene glycol. The hydroextraction is carried out at $+4°C$ until 10–15 ml of liquid has been obtained. Then a dialysis is carried out at $+4°C$ with a buffered phosphate solution under magnetic stirring for 1 hour. The final liquid obtained is ready to be seeded into systems that reveal the presence of viruses.

3.3.2.3. Limitations of the Method

This method is simple but relatively time-consuming, since it requires about 20 hours. However, it allows one to obtain small volumes of concentrate, according to Farrah et al (1977, 1978), yields are approximately 70%.

3.3.3. Secondary Concentration by AdsorptionElution on Iron Oxide

3.3.3.1. Principles

The oxides of iron, particularly magnetite (Fe_3O_4), can be considered to be good adsorbents for the viruses present in water. According to Bitton (1980), the adsorption of poliovirus on magnetite is efficient at a pH between 5 and 8. The viruses that are adsorbed on iron oxide particles can be eluted secondarily with the aid of an alkaline protein solution.

3.3.3.2. Operations

The viral solution to be concentrated is first adjusted to pH 7.2. Then the iron oxide is added in a ratio of 1.5 g to 1000 ml. The solution is gently and intermittently stirred with a glass rod for 30 minutes. With the aid of a magnet, the iron oxide is collected and maintained on the bottom of the vessel, and the liquid above is eliminated. The bottom layer of iron oxide onto which the viruses are adsorbed is taken up with a small volume of eluting solution such as a 2% solution of casein (pH 8.5). After slow stirring for 10 to 15 minutes, the casein solution is taken off while a magnet holds the iron oxide on the bottom of the vessel. This solution constitutes the viral concentrate which, after neutralization at pH 7–7.2, will be tested on the systems that reveal the presence of viruses.

3.3.3.3. Limitations of the Method

The method of secondary concentration by adsorptionelution on iron oxide is extremely simple, economical, and very rapid. One can obtain low-volume concentrates, which theoretically do not show any toxicity for the cells. It has been used to concentrate viruses from water samples with a yield that varies from 60 to 80% (Rao et al, 1981).

3.4. DECONTAMINATION OF THE SAMPLES

The samples obtained by the methods described above all contain appreciable quantities of bacteria and microscopic fungi that must be inactivated before the cell cultures are inoculated.

Theoretically, either of two techniques can be applied: addition of antibiotics or treatment with chloroform. However, due to the presence of antibiotic-resistant microorganisms, it is preferable to follow a treatment with a solvent for lipids and by addition of a blend of antibiotics.

3.4.1. Treatment with Chloroform

Within the specific framework of a search for enteroviruses (viruses without envelopes), the addition of chloroform permits one to inactivate all microorganisms containing lipids (bacteria and yeasts). This is thus an effective means of decontamination, which is obtained by adding 30% more of chloroform to the sample and then getting good contact between the two phases by rapid mixing for 30 minutes at ambient temperature.

After the mixture has settled, the chloroform phase is discarded and the traces of chloroform left in the aqueous phase are carried away by bubbling in sterilized air or nitrogen. The work should be carried out in a hood to avoid the toxic fumes of chloroform.

3.4.2. Treatment with Antibiotics

Treatment by antibiotics consists of adding to the samples a mixture of molecules that are active against bacteria and microscopic fungi at doses that are not toxic for the cell cultures.

Table 3.2 gives an example of an aqueous solution of antibiotics currently utilized.

This solution is added in a ratio of 0.1 ml per milliliter of sample and should be mixed and left in contact for 3 hours at 37°C before inoculating susceptible systems. (Penicillin acts only on bacteria in division.)

3.5. DETOXIFICATION OF THE SAMPLES

The concentration methods for viruses carry along any matter in suspension and numerous types of ions, molecules, and macromolecules (heavy metals, detergents, hydrocarbons, etc), which may be toxic for the cell cultures and consequently would

Table 3.2. Composition of a solution of antibiotics for decontaminating viral concentrates

Active molecule	Concentration
Sodium benzylpenicillinate	100,000 U/ml
Neomycin	0.015 g/ml
Streptomycin sulfate	0.1 g/ml
Amphotericin B (fungizone)	0.005 mg/ml

prevent viral multiplication. One way to lower this risk of toxicity is to dilute the sample, although unfortunately, the volume of the inoculum must be increased considerably.

Two complementary techniques permit a good resolution of this problem

1. Centrifugation at 8500 *g* or greater (Hejkal et al, 1982), which eliminates suspended matter that often provides a support for toxic molecules: this centrifugation, applied to the elution liquid and not to the untreated water sample, does not entail a significant lowering of the viral titer.

2. Chloroform extraction by successive washings of the sample: in this case, it is sufficient to repeat three to five times the technique of decontamination by chloroform just described. Such an operation might diminish the toxicity for the cell culture by at least 70% (Rolland, 1981). However, it is sometimes difficult to break up the final chloroform emulsion and to eliminate the last traces of chloroform.

Finally, in the presence of a sample that may be toxic, it is recommended that one wash the cell layer by very gentle stirring with several milliliters of PBS solution to which has been added 2% fetal calf serum (Berg et al, 1984).

REFERENCES

American Public Health Association (1979) "Standard Methods for the Examination of Water and Wastewater: Detection of Enteric Viruses in Water and Wastewater," 14th ed. APHA, Washington, D.C., pp. 969–975.

Belfort, G., and Dziewulski, D. M. (1982) Concentration of viruses from aqueous environments: A review of the methodology. In "Water Reuse," E. J. Middlebrooks, Ed. Ann Arbor Science Publishers, Ann Arbor, MI, pp. 679–750.

Berg, G., Safferman, R. S., Dahling, D. R., Berman, D., and Hurst C. Y. (1984) U.S. Environmental Protection Agency Manual of Methods for Virology. E.P.A. Publication EPA-600/4-84-013, Cincinnati, OH.

Beytout, D., Charrier, F., Laveran, H., and Monghal, M. (1977) Méthode de détection de faibles quantités de virus dans les eaux d'alimentation. *Ann. Microbiol. (Institut Pasteur)*, **182**, 255–262.

Bitton, G. (1980) "Introduction to Environmental Virology." Wiley, New York.

Bitton, G., Feldberg, B. N., and Farrah, S. R. (1979) Concentration of enterovirus from seawater and tap water by organic flocculation using nonfat dry milk and casein. *Water Air Soil Pollut.* **12**, 187–195.

Cliver, D. O. (1967) Enterovirus detection by membrane chromatography. In "Transmission of Viruses by the Water Route," G. Berg, Ed. Wiley, New York, pp. 139–149.

Dahling, D. R., and Wright, B. A. (1984) Processing and transport of environmental virus samples. *Appl. Environ. Microbiol.* **47**, 1272–1276.

Farrah, S. R., Goyal, S. M., Gerba, C. P., Wallis, C., and Shaffer, P. T. B. (1978) Concentration of poliovirus from tap water onto membrane filters with aluminum chloride at ambient pH levels. *Appl. Environ. Microbiol.* **35**, 624–626.

Farrah, S. R., Goyal, S. M., Gerba, C. P., Wallis, C., and Melnick, J. L. (1977) Concentration of enterovirus from estuarine water. *Appl. Environ. Microbiol.* **33**, 1192–1196.

Farrah, S. R., Gerba, C. P., Wallis, C., and Melnick, J. L. (1976) Concentration of viruses from large volume of tap water using pleated membrane filters. *Appl. Environ. Microbiol.* **31**, 221–226.

Fattal, B., and Katzenelson, E. (1976) Evaluation of gauze pad method to recover viruses from water. *Water Res.* **10**, 1135–1140.

Foliguet, J. M., Lavillaureix, J., and Schwartzbrod, L. (1973) Virus et eaux. II. Mise en evidence des virus dans le milieu hydrique. *Rev. Epidemiol. Med. Soc. Sante Publique*, **21**, 185–259.

Gerba, C. P. (1984) Applied and theoretical aspects of virus adsorption to surfaces. In "Advances in Applied Microbiology," A. P. Laskin, Ed. Academic Press, New York, pp. 133–168.

Guttman-Bass, N., Hostovsky, T., Lugten, M., and Armon, R. (1985) A comparison of current methods of poliovirus concentration from tap water. *Water Res.* **19**, 85–88.

Hejkal, T. W., Gerba, C. P., and Rao, V. C. (1982) Reduction of cytotoxicity in virus concentrates from environmental samples. *Appl. Environ. Microbiol.* **43**, 731–733.

Hurst, C. J., Dahling, D. R., Safferman, R. S., and Goyke, T. (1984) Comparison of commercial beef extracts and similar materials for recovering viruses from environmental samples. *Can. J. Microbiol.* **30**, 1253–1260.

Joret, J. C., and Block, J. C. (1981) Survie des entérovirus adsorbes sur microfibre de verre au cours d'un transport postal. *J. Can. Microbiol.* **27**, 246–248.

Joret, J. C., Block, J. C., Lucena-Gutierrez, F., Schwartzbrod, L., Hugues, B., and Plissier, A. (1980) Virus concentration from secondary wastewater: Comparative study between epoxy fiberglass and glass powder adsorbants. *Eur. J. Appl. Microbiol. Biotechnol.* **10**, 245–252.

Katzenelson, E., Fattal, B., and Hostovesky, T. (1976) Organic flocculation: An efficient second-step concentration method for the detection of viruses in tap water. *Appl. Environ. Microbiol.* **32**, 638–639.

Keswick, B. H. (1983) Survival of enteric viruses adsorbed on electropositive filters. *Appl. Environ. Microbiol.* **46**, 501–502.

Melnick, J. L., Safferman, R., Rao, V. C., GOYAL, S., Berg, G., Dahling, D. R., Wright, B. A., Akin, E., Stetler, R., Sorber, C., Moore, B., Sobsey, M. D., Moore, R., Lewis, A. L., and Wellings, F. M. (1984) Round robin investigation of methods for the recovery of poliovirus from drinking water. *Appl. Environ. Microbiol.* **47**, 144–150.

Payment, P., Fortin, S., and Trudel, M. (1984) Ferric chloride flocculation for nonflocculating beef extract preparations. *Appl. Environ. Microbiol.* **47**, 591–592.

Rao, V. C., Waghmare, S. V., and Lakhe, S. B. (1981) Detection of viruses in drinking water using magnetic iron oxide. *Appl. Environ. Microbiol.* **42**, 421–426.

Rolland, D. (1981) Flux de virus entériques dans les eaux usées brutes et traitées d'une station d'épuration biologique. Master's thesis, Universite de Metz.

Sarrette, B., Danglot, C., and Vilagines, R. (1977) A new and simple method for recuperation of enterovirus from water. *Water Res.* **11**, 355–358.

Schwartzbrod, L., and Lucena-Gutierrez, F. (1978) Concentration des entérovirus dans les eaux par adsorption sur poudre de verre: Proposition d'un appareillage simplifié. *Microbia*, **4**, 55–58.

Shields, P. A., and Farrah, S. R. (1983) Influence of salts on electrostatic interaction between poliovirus and membrane filters. *Appl. Environ. Microbiol.* **45**, 526–531.

Sobsey, M. D., and Glass, J. S. (1980) Poliovirus concentration from tap water with electropositive adsorbent filters. *Appl. Environ. Microbio.* **40**, 201–210.

Sobsey, M. D., Wallis, C., Henderson, M., and Melnick, J. L. (1973) Concentration of enteroviruses from large volumes of water. *Appl. Microbiol.* **26**, 529–534.

Vilagines, P. (1980) Concentration des entérovirus sur poudre de verre en lit fluidisé à partir d'échantillons de volumes variables d'eaux d'origines diverses. Mise au point d'une nouvelle méthode de reconcentration. Master's thesis, Universite Rene Descartes, Paris.

Vilagines, P., Sarrette, B., Danglot, C., and Vilagines, R. (1979) Détection d'entérovirus par concentration sur poudre de verre en lit fluidisé à partir d'échantillons de 500 litres d'eaux superficielles. *Bull. Acad. Nat. Med.* **163**, 668–673.

Wallis, C., and Melnick, J. L. (1967) Concentration of viruses on aluminum and calcium salts. *Am. J. Epidemiol.* **85**, 459–468.

Chapter 4

SYSTEMS FOR THE DETECTION OF VIRUSES

The nature, structure, and physical chemistry of viruses are such that viral detection presents a certain number of difficulties or anomalies. Because of their small size, viruses cannot be observed with the classical optical microscope, but they may be studied by means of electron microscopy (EM). However, this method necessitates costly apparatus and techniques such as ultracentrifugation and sophisticated sample preparation. There are two more drawbacks to using EM: the technique permits a morphological diagnosis only when the structure of the viral particle is conserved, and the sensitivity of EM is inferior to that obtained when viruses are cultured in a receptive host. EM is usually positive only when the sample contains at least 10^6 infectious viral particles. Because viruses are strictly cellular parasites, they can multiply only in living cells. Three available sources of cells are the whole animal, the embryonated egg, and in vitro cell cultures.

In the virology of water systems, the viruses that are most frequently searched for (ie, enteroviruses, adenoviruses, and reoviruses) are detected essentially from cell cultures. Inoculation in the animal is used very rarely and then only for certain enteroviruses that do not multiply in cell systems.

This chapter focuses primarily on the principal system for detection of viruses, that is, in vitro cell cultures and more specifically on the use of animals.

4.1. CELL CULTURES

The first cell cultures were developed in the beginning of this century by Carrel (1912). In 1954 Dulbecco and Vogt demonstrated that by treating fragments of tissue with trypsin, it was possible to obtain a suspension of individual cells. These cells, in the presence of a nutritive liquid, were able to attach themselves to the walls of a glass vessel and to multiply on it. Scherer et al (1953) showed that it was possible to cultivate certain cells indefinitely, and in 1955 Eagle perfected synthetic culture media permitting a certain standardization of the techniques for cell culture.

An in vitro cell culture is a system in which cells that are placed in an artificial environment are capable of multiplying without conserving the structural organization of the original tissue. From such cell cultures, Enders et al (1949) obtained the multiplication of the poliomyelitic virus and demonstrated that this multiplication induces an alteration and then specific cellular destruction. In fact, a large number of viruses are capable of multiplying and provoking characteristic lesions (cytopathic effect, or CPE), the observation of which permits the detection of the viral replication.

Three principal elements are involved in cell cultures: the supports on which the cells multiply, the culture media, and the cells themselves.

4.1.1. The Vessels for Culture

Normally, an undisturbed cell suspension in a nutritive liquid will sediment, and in a few hours the cells will attach themselves tightly to the walls of the vessel. In a second step, if conditions are favorable, the units will multiply and more or less rapidly form a continuous cell layer.

4.1.1.1. Characteristics of the Vessels

Numerous vessels have been studied, as well as the interactions between the cells and vessels. It has thus been possible to establish the essential characteristics of a good vessel based on its different roles.

The vessels should permit:

A microscope examination of the cells; therefore vessels are made of either glass or transparent plastic, through which light can pass.

The growth of cells on its surface; thus there can be no cytotoxic effect.

The stability of the nutritive medium that bathes the cells; thus vessels require a stable and definite chemical composition, and they should not harbor acidic or basic products, which are capable of varying the pH of the medium.

A sterile culture; it is essential that vessels actually withstand sterilization procedures and remain hermetically closed.

Eventual reuse; thus it should be easy to wash and sterilize the vessels, and these operations should not alter the general properties of the equipment.

4.1.1.2. Types of Vessel

Vessels are selected on the basis of the foregoing criteria, as well as type of culture desired and the quantity of cells to be produced.

When cells multiply, they exhibit a phenomenon called contact inhibition; that is, they stop multiplying as soon as they enter into contact with one another. Therefore, the larger the surface to be covered, the greater will be the quantity of cells produced.

The size and the nature of the vessels also depends on the production of large quantities of cells or of numerous units of cell cultures necessary for a virological analysis.

a. Vessels for Massive Production of Cells. These vessels, which will naturally be chosen as large as possible, are in general made of either flat or cylindrical flasks, or of microbeads.

The flat flasks are Pyrex or plastic. The cells attach themselves and then multiply on the flask's lower walls. The receptacles used most frequently are:

250 ml flasks (60 and 75 cm^2)
650 ml flasks (150 cm^2)
1 liter Roux bottles (200 cm^2)(Fig. 4.1)
3.5 liter Lepine bottles (600 cm^2)

The Pyrex cylindrical flasks present a large surface for culture (500 cm^2) and can be submitted to a very slow but continuous rotation (Roller culture). The cells can thus

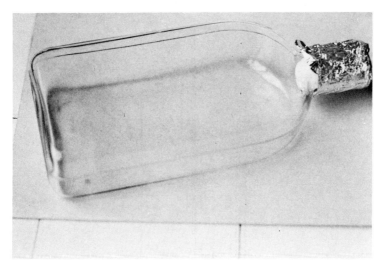

Figure 4.1. A Roux bottle.

attach themselves to the whole surface of the cylinder and be bathed regularly by the medium (Fig. 4.2).

The microbeads are DEAE Sephadex A50 microbeads; their diameter after expansion in a medium varies from 160 to 220 μm. The cells attach themselves to the microbeads, which are in suspension in the nutritive medium. Interestingly, this type of culture allows a massive production of cells by considerably increasing the surface

Figure 4.2. A culture on rollers.

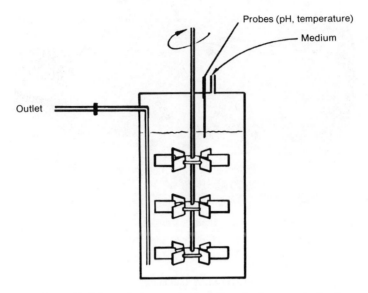

Figure 4.3. Scheme of a fermentation device for cell cultures on microbeads.

available for culture. Thus, 1 gram of DEAE Sephadex contains around 5×10^6 beads, which equals a surface of 6000 cm². The production of cells is carried out in the interior of fermentation devices (Fig. 4.3). It should be noted that other supports have been proposed, such as particles of polystyrene and polyacrylamide or glass beads (Varani et al, 1983).

b. Vessels for Virological Analysis. To carry out the operations of isolation, quantification, and identification of viruses, it is necessary to have a large number of flasks or culture tubes available. The vessels most often used are:

12×120 mm plastic or Pyrex test tubes placed in a vertical position, such that the cells multiply on the bottom of the tube

Glass or plastic 60 ml (25 cm²) flat bottom flasks

50 or 100 mm plastic petri dishes (20 or 78 cm²)

Plastic multiple-culture dishes with 24 wells, each well having a culture surface of 1.9 cm²

12×8 cm microplates—plastic plates having 96 wells, each with a flat bottom and a diameter of 7 mm (Fig. 4.4)

Leighton tubes—16×160 mm Pyrex tubes having a flat bottom and a glass or plastic removable slide on which the cell culture is carried out (Fig. 4.5); the slide is then lifted off, fixed, and stained.

4.1.1.3. Preparation of the Vessels

Most of the vessels described above can be made of either glass or plastic. Plastic vessels, which are nonreusable, are sold ready for use in a sterile wrapping. Sterilization is carried out on an industrial scale by the action of ethylene oxide or gamma rays.

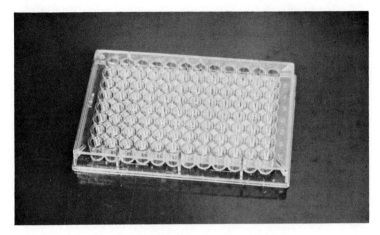

Figure 4.4. A microplate.

Glass vessels are reusable, and they should thus be washed and sterilized (cf Chapter 2). The preparation of the glass material is different according to whether it is new, used but not contaminated, or used and contaminated by viruses.

a. New Material. Each new glass vessel is first immersed for 12 hours in 5% HCl then rinsed 10 times with tap water. It is then ready for washing and sterilization.

b. Uncontaminated Used Material. Such material is first immersed for 12 hours in a detergent solution (7 × type or DDN), then rinsed 10 times with tap water, left in deionized water for 12 hours, and rinsed 10 times in deionized water.

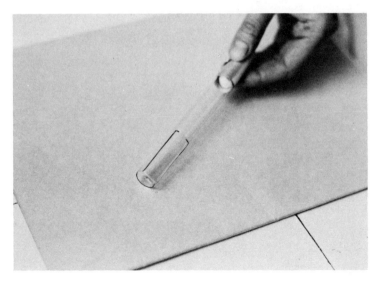

Figure 4.5. A Leighton tube; its removable slide permits the investigator to perform histological studies.

Table 4.1. Composition of different media for cell cultures

	Eagle's medium and modified Eagle's medium			
	Basal Eagle's medium (BEM), modified with Earle's salts mg/liter	Minimum essential Eagle's medium (MEM), modified with Earle's salts mg/liter	Medium L-15, modified mg/liter	Medium 199 with Earle's salts mg/liter
l-alanine	21.06		225.0	25.00
l-arginine		126.4	500.0	70.00
l-asparagine, H₂O			250.0	
l-aspartic acid				30.00
l-cysteine			120.0	0.099
l-cystine	14.21	28.42		23.66
l-glutamic acid				66.82
l-glutamine	292.3	292.3	300.0	100.0
Glutathion				0.05
Glycine			200.0	50.00
l-histidine, H₂O	10.50	41.90	250.0	21.88
l-hydroxyproline				10.00
l-isoleucine	26.23	52.50	125.0	20.00
l-leucine	26.23	52.50	125.0	60.00
l-lysine	36.53	73.06	93.70	70.00
l-methionine	7.46	14.90	75.0	15.00
l-phenylalanine	16.51	33.03	125.0	25.00
l-proline				40.00
l-serine			200.0	25.00
l-threonine	23.82	47.64	300.0	30.00
l-trytophane	4.08	10.20	20.0	10.00
l-tyrosine	18.11	36.22	300.0	40.00
l-valine	23.43	46.90	100.0	25.00
l-ascorbic acid				0.05
Biotine	1.00			0.01
Calciferol				0.10
D-Ca-pantothenate	1.00	1.00	1.00	0.01
D-galactose			900.0	
Choline chloride	1.00	1.00	1.00	0.50

Folic acid	1.00	1.00	1.00	0.01
I-inositol	2.00	2.00	2.00	0.05
Menadione				0.019
Nicotinamide	1.00	1.00	1.00	0.025
Nicotinic acid				0.025
P-aminobenzoic acid				0.05
Pyridoxal	1.00	1.00	1.00	0.025
Pyridoxine				0.025
Riboflavin	0.10	0.10	0.10	0.01
Thiamine	1.00	1.00	1.00	0.01
Thiamine monophosphate, 2H$_2$O				
α-tocopherol				0.01
Vitamin A				0.115
CaCl$_2$ · 2H$_2$O	264.9	264.9	185.5	264.9
Fe(NO$_3$)$_3$ · 9H$_2$O			0.10	0.10
KCl	400.0	400.0	400.0	400.0
KH$_2$PO$_4$			60.0	
MgSO$_4$ · 7H$_2$O	200.0	200.0	400.0	200.0
NaCl	6800	6800	8000	6800
NaHCO$_3$	1680	2000		2200
NaH$_2$PO$_4$ · 2H$_2$O	158.3	158.3		158.3
Na$_2$HPO$_4$			190.0	
Adenine				10.00
5-AMP				0.20
ATP (sodium salt)				10.00
Cholesterol				0.20
2-deoxyribose				0.50
Glucose	1000	1000	1000	1000
Gluanine				0.30
Hypoxanthine				0.30
Ribose				0.50
Phenol red	17.00	17.00	10.00	17.00
Sodium acetate				36.71
Sodium pyruvate			550.0	
Thymine				0.30
Tween 80				5.00
Uracil				0.30
Xanthine				0.30

c. Contaminated Used Material. Before washing, this material should be decontaminated by sterilization in an autoclave at 121°C for 20 minutes. It can then be washed and sterilized.

After washing, the vessels are dried and stoppered with cotton wads that are wrapped first with hydrophilic gauze and then with Kraft paper or aluminum foil. The units are then sterilized by autoclaving at 121°C for 20 minutes.

During cell culture, the vessels should be kept airtight with either metal or Bakelite caps or rubber stoppers (plasma quality) that do not contain any toxic substances. The capsules and stoppers are sterilized separately in an autoclave at 121°C for 20 minutes.

The multiple-culture dishes and the microplates can be made airtight with covers. Nevertheless, most often these vessels as well as petri dishes are not hermetically sealed but are placed in incubators with an atmosphere rich in carbon dioxide.

4.1.2. Culture Media

The cells, attached to their vessels, must be grown or maintained in an adequate nutritive medium.

Every kind of medium has as a basic component a buffered saline solution to which glucose has been added (Earle, 1943; Hanks and Wallace, 1949). The buffer solution is essential for maintaining the pH at a value compatible with cellular life, assuring a correct osmotic pressure, and providing the essential mineral ions. It is supplemented with various nutritive substances. The media are classified according to their designation as growth media or survival media.

4.1.2.1. Growth Media

Growth media should contain the necessary elements for the multiplication of the cells. In current practice, investigators use only synthetic media containing amino acids, vitamins, growth factors, nucleosides, and coenzymes, all dissolved in a basic saline solution. Among the numerous proposed media (Table 4.1), the most widely used are the basal and minimum Eagle's media (Eagle, 1955, 1959), medium 199 (Morgan et al, 1950), medium LI5 (Leibovitz, 1963), and medium RPMI (Moore et al, 1967).

All these growth media are given 10% animal serum such as fetal or neonatal calf serum, decomplemented by heating at 56°C for 30 minutes. Each lot of calf serum should be pretested to prevent cytotoxicity.

4.1.2.2. Survival Media

Survival media contain the minimal substances necessary for cellular life in a stationary phase. There are two types: liquid media and gel media.

Liquid media consist of the synthetic and semisynthetic media described above, to which are added in general 2% animal serum.

Agar media are used for the isolation and quantification of viruses by the plaque technique. Several formulas for these media have been proposed. Their compositions are indicated in Table 4.2.

Table 4.2. Composition of survival agar media

Medium without vital stain		Medium with vital stain	
Solution A		Solution A	
Eagle's MEM	100 ml	Eagle's MEM without phenol red	415 ml
7.5% NaHCO$_3$ solution	20 ml	7.5% NaHCO$_3$ solution	30 ml
1% MgCl$_2$ solution	10 ml	1% MgCl$_2$ solution	10 ml
Glutamine solution (200 mM/ml)	10 ml	Decomplemented fetal calf serum	20 ml
Decomplemented fetal calf serum	20 ml	0.1% neutral red solution	15 ml
Solution of penicillin (5000 U/ml)		Solution of penicillin (100,000 U/ml)	
and streptomycin (5 mg/ml)	20 ml	and streptomycin (125 mg/ml)	1 ml
Kanamycin solution (10 mg/ml)	10 ml	Tetracycline solution (25 mg/ml)	0.5 ml
Fungizone solution (250 μg/ml)	10 ml	Fungizone solution (5 mg/ml)	0.2 ml
Distilled water Q.S.P.			
Solution B		Solution B	
Bacto-agar	7.5 g	Bacto-agar	15 g
Distilled water Q.S.P.	500 ml	Distilled water Q.S.P.	500 ml

Solution B is first heated to 120°C for 15 min then cooled on a water bath at 56°C. It is then mixed with Solution A previously brought to 37°C. The mixture just obtained is immediately distributed over the cell cultures.

Both growth and survival culture media contain a color indicator (phenol red), which allows detection of variations in pH. Furthermore a solution of antibiotics (Table 4.3) is added in a ratio of 5 ml per liter just before the medium is to be used. Sterilization and verification of the medium's sterility, of course, must be completed before the addition of antibiotic solution.

4.1.2.3. Preparation and Sterilization of the Culture Media

The preparation of the culture media is relatively simple; however, it should be done with great care to prevent contamination.

The media are generally prepared from a liquid concentrate or from a powder, which is dissolved in an adequate quantity of deionized water that has been sterilized by autoclave. The necessary volume of animal serum is then added. In certain cases, according to the manufacturer and the type of medium, it is necessary to complement the solution thus obtained with compounds such as sodium bicarbonate (buffer effect) or L-glutamine (whose conservation is difficult in liquid concentrates).

The pH is then checked and raised if necessary by bubbling in carbon dioxide or by the addition of sodium hydroxide to the desired value (7–7.2). It should be noted that the pH increases about 0.2 unit during the course of sterilization by filtration.

Table 4.3. Composition of a solution of antibiotics for culture media

Ingredient	Amount
Sodium benzylpenicillinate	5 million units
Streptomycin	5 g
Neomycin	5 g
Water, USP	400 ml

Figure 4.6. The complete sterilization apparatus.

Several media can be sterilized in an autoclave before the addition of calf serum, but media containing thermolabile substances must be sterilized by filtration. This can be achieved with the aid of pressurized nitrogen, which pushes the medium through a prefilter and three filtering membranes composed of cellulose ester with respective porosities of 1.2, 0.45, and 0.22 μm, separated from one another by a gauze disk.

The diameters of the filters and of their support are chosen as a function of the quantity of medium to be filtered. Thus, membranes of 142 mm diameter are necessary to sterilize more than 3 liters of a medium containing 10% serum. The whole sterilization apparatus (Fig. 4.6) is composed of a reservoir of medium supporting the pressure, connected at one end with a tank of nitrogen and on the other with the filter. A gas distribution tank is connected to the filtration support by a rubber tube.

The filtration support, which is equipped with different filtering membranes and connected to the distribution tank, should be presterilized in an autoclave for 20 minutes at 121°C.

The filtered medium is directly distributed into sterile flasks of 100, 250, 500, or 1000 ml. A group of each constitutes a batch whose sterility should be controlled.

4.1.2.4. Controls of the Sterility of the Media

To ensure the detection of any possible bacterial or fungal contamination, it is essential to verify rigorously the sterility of each batch of medium. These controls are carried out in two ways.

1. At the start and at the end of the filtration, two tubes of resazurine thioglycolate broth (detection of anaerobic and aerobic microorganisms) and two tubes of trypticase–soy medium (detection of aerobic microorganisms and yeast) are

inoculated, each with 1 ml of filtered medium. The two sets of tubes are incubated at 37 and at 22°C, respectively, for 5 days.

2. After filtration, all the flasks of medium are kept at ambient temperature and in the dark for a maximum of 5 days, to avoid glutamine degradation.

If at the end of the observation period the tubes of broth present no microbial development and the flasks of medium are not turbid, the batch of medium is considered to be sterile. It is then stored at +4°C to await being used.

4.1.3. The Cells

Classically three categories of cell systems can be distinguished: primary cells, established cell lines, and diploid cells. These cells differ from one another by their characteristics and their origin.

4.1.3.1. The Different Types of Cell Culture

a. Primary Cells. These cells stem directly from an animal organ (monkey kidney; pork kidney; rabbit kidney, amnion, thyroid, etc). These epithelial cells undergo contact inhibition and are cultured into monolayers. For example, for monkey kidney cells, the life span of the cell layer (depending on the mode of culture, defined in Section 4.1.3.2) is approximately 15 to 20 days. During this period they keep the general characteristics of the cells of their tissue of origin, in particular the diploid nature. Such cell cultures are either used directly for the detection of viruses by inoculation with an aliquot of a sample, or subcultured (no more than twice).

In current practice, monkey kidney cells, which are the most widely used for the detection of enteric viruses, can be obtained from specialized laboratories in the form of concentrated suspensions. These cells are placed into culture and incubated at 37 ± 0.5°C after addition of growth medium in a suitable proportion.

b. Established Cell Lines. These do not come directly from tissue but have been maintained and subcultivated in most virology laboratories for many years. A cell line can be considered to be established if, a priori, it can be subcultivated at 37 ± 0.5°C indefinitely. These cell lines present chromosomal anomalies affecting either the number or the structure of the chromosomes.

Numerous established cell lines have been developed. They originate from either normal or tumoral tissues. Among those most frequently used in the virological analysis of waters one can cite the following:

Lines of human origin
    KB cells (from carcinoma of the mouth)
    HeLa cells (from an epidermoid carcinoma of the cervix)
    Hep 2 cells (from carcinoma of the larynx)
    RD cells (from rhabdomyosarcoma)
Lines of simian origin: Vero, BGM, and BSC_1 cells (from the kidney of *Cercopithecus aethiops*)

Such cell lines can be obtained from specialized laboratories. They should be regularly tested to detect any possible contamination by mycoplasma.

c. Diploid Cells. In these cell strains, at least 75% of the cells have conserved the same karyotype as the normal cells of the species from which they were derived. Diploid cells exhibit contact inhibition and can be subcultured but have a limited life span. In fact, the in vitro life of such cells, obtained from a tissue (usually embryonic), shows three phases: a primary phase of culture, followed by a phase of exponential growth during which the cells maintain their diploid character, and a phase of old age in which cellular alterations appear and mitotic processes slow down, which is a prelude to cellular death.

Contrary to the case of established cell lines, where the number of generations is not significant, the number of generations for the diploid strain is important because it loses its properties and dies after a set number of generations.

Of the human varieties, the most frequently used diploid strains are derived from human embryos, namely the WI 38, MRC 5, and IMR 90 lines.

In current practice these cells should be subcultivated at $37 \pm 0.5°C$ by doubling two times per week. They can thus be used for only 30 to 50 successive generations. However, it is possible to use a diploid line for a longer time because each doubling furnishes a very large quantity of cells, which can be maintained by freezing in liquid nitrogen (cf Section 4.1.3.4).

4.1.3.2. Upkeep of Cell Cultures

The upkeep of cell cultures in the laboratory varies according to the type of culture desired; however, it is possible to pick out a certain number of fundamental points.

A cell culture is incubated at $37 \pm 0.5°C$.

The culture should be observed regularly with an inverse microscope to determine the state or the development of the cell layer.

The variations in pH of the culture medium should be carefully noted. Then, when a cellular suspension in nutritive medium is placed in a flask, the cells attach themselves to the vessel walls and multiply. In the first step, the medium becomes basic as a result of the dissociation of sodium bicarbonate and the liberation of hydroxyl ions. Then progressively and at thefsame rate as the development of the culture, the nutritive medium is exhausted; this is accompanied by the increasing acidification of the medium due to the production of acidic substances during cellular metabolism.

When acidification occurs (turning the phenol red to yellow), it is necessary to replace the medium either with an identical growth medium or, if there is a continuous monolayer, with a survival medium. In such cases subculturing by trypsination (usually every 7 days) can be done. If such subculturing must be delayed, or if it is necessary to maintain the cells for too long a time, the repeated and regular renewal of the medium will permit one to maintain the cells alive for 10 to 30 days.

4.1.3.3. Subculture by Trypsination

Subculturing of cells requires dissociation of the cell layer to obtain individualized cells that when placed into new growth medium, will multiply to give new cell layers. Several dissociation techniques have been proposed, using either enzymes (trypsin) or complexing chemicals (versene or EDTA), or a mixture of enzyme and complexing agent (trypsin–versene). One of the best methods is the latter, which is described below.

Table 4.4. Composition of a wash solution

Ingredient	Amount
NaCl	8 g
KCl	0.2 g
Na_2HPO_4	1.15 g
KH_2PO_4	0.2 g
Distilled, deionized water	1000 ml

a. Dissociation of the Cell Layer by Means of a Trypsin Versene Mixture. Trypsin is a proteolytic enzyme capable of digesting the protein material that binds the cells to one another either in a tissue or in cell monolayers. This enzymatic procedure does not provoke cellular lesions and thus permits one to obtain a suspension of living cells that are perfectly individualized. The versene completes this action by complexing the di and trivalent ions that participate in the intercellular bonds. This technique consists in first pipetting off the medium above a continuous cell monolayer. A washing solution (15 ml) that has been sterilized in an autoclave at $121°C$ for 20 minutes (Table 4.4) is introduced and left in contact with the cell layer for 5 minutes. After stirring, the solution is taken off and replaced by 15 ml of a versene–trypsin solution (0.25 g of trypsin and 0.02 g of versene for 100 ml of wash solution), previously sterilized by filtration. Both the media and the reactants have previously been heated to $37 \pm 0.5°C$. The mixing is done at 37°C for a variable time (in general, 410 minutes) according to the type of cells. When the cell layer starts to detach itself, the solution is immediately removed by pipetting and replaced with 20 ml of nutritive medium. Through successive aspirations and replacements, the cell layer becomes totally detached, whereupon it is homogenized to obtain a dispersed cellular suspension, which should finally be quantified through cell counting.

b. Cellular Count. The counting of the cells allows one not only to determine the cellular density of the suspension but also to ascertain the physiological state of the cells. One method consists of diluting the cell suspension (eg, to 1:10) in a survival medium containing 10% of solution with 0.4% erythrosin B. After homogenization, several drops are pipetted into a counting chamber. Microscopic observation will reveal either dead cells, which are colored pink by the erythrosin, or living cells, which are not stained. Less than 2% dead cells indicates good conditions for culture and trypsination. On the contrary, a cellular mortality of 10% or more reflects a poor physiological state of the culture or a drastic trypsination effect. Counting quantifies living cells only: specifically those present in eight bands (or 10 μl) of the counting chamber.

If in eight bands, X cells have been counted, the number N of cells per milliliter of initial suspension will be obtained by the following relation:

$$N = X \times 10^3$$

c. Distribution of the Cells. The cellular suspension thus counted should be distributed throughout the supports. The quantity of cells to be inoculated depends obviously on the surface of the support, but also on the type of cell. The density is on the average between $1-3 \times 10^5$ cells per milliliter for the primary cell lines and $1-2 \times 10^5$ for the established lines. Table 4.5 indicates as an example the cellular density and the volume of medium necessary for different supports for BGM cells.

Table 4.5. Cell density seeded according to the type of support

Type of support	Volume of medium	BGM Cell density per milliliter $(\times 10^5)$
12 × 120 mm tube	1 ml	1
Leighton tube	2 ml	2
25 cm² flask	7 ml	2.8
60 cm² flask	20 ml	2
200 cm² Roux flask	80 ml	1.8
19 cm² petri dish	6 ml	2.5
78 cm² petri dish	20 ml	2.5
Microplate (96 holes)	0.2 ml	2
Multiple dish with 24 wells	1.5–2 ml per well	1.5
Multiple dish with 6 wells	2 ml per well	1.5

The cells obtained after trypsination are introduced according to the cellular density desired into a sterile flask containing an adequate quantity of growth medium. The suspension is then homogenized by magnetic stirring and distributed (Fig. 4.7) by means of a Cornwall syringe adapted to the flask; the vessels are sealed with rubber stoppers or capsules. They are then put into incubation at $37 \pm 0.5°C$.

In the case of petri dishes or microplates, the incubation is carried out at $37 \pm 0.5°C$ in special enclosures (CO_2 incubator) in an atmosphere enriched to 5% CO_2.

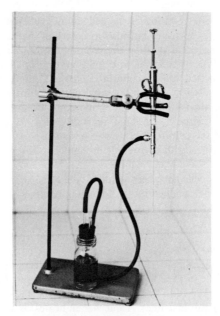

Figure 4.7. Cell distribution apparatus.

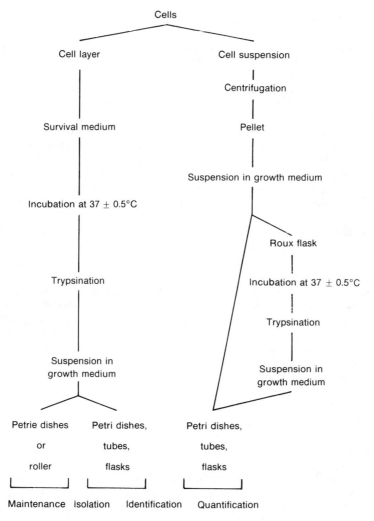

Figure 4.8. Procedures for maintaining and subculturing cells.

It is recommended that the recipients not be moved for the first 5 to 6 hours of incubation, to allow the cells to become thoroughly attached to the vessel. After 24 to 48 hours of incubation, observation by microscope should show numerous micro-colonies of growing cells. After 3 to 5 days the confluence of these colonies leads to the formation of a cell layer, which then is ready to be trypsinated or used for a search for viruses by seeding of an inoculum.

It is obvious that all these cell culture procedures should be carried out under conditions of absolute sterility. Furthermore, all the media and solutions that are used should be reheated to a temperature of $37 \pm 0.5°C$ before use.

Figure 4.8 summarizes the diverse operations carried out during the maintenance and subculturing of the cells.

4.1.3.4. Cell Storage

The established cell lines, some of which are used only occasionally in the laboratory, as well as the diploid cells, are conserved to avoid the need to replicate subcultures later.

If the cells are to be maintained for a relatively brief time (a few weeks), it is sufficient to place the culture flask at ambient temperature after adding some survival medium.

If the conservation is to be longer, it is necessary to freeze a cellular suspension, to which has been added a cryoprotector such as glycerol or dimethyl sulfoxide (DMSO), either at $-70°C$ in a freezer or at $-196°C$ in liquid nitrogen.

The technique consists of introducing into a sterile Pyrex ampoule the cells, which are in suspension in modified Eagle's medium to which is added 10% fetal calf serum and 10% protecting agent such as glycerol or DMSO. The cellular suspension should contain 4 to 5×10^6 cells per milliliter.

The ampoule is then sealed, chilled slowly with a lowering of $1°C$ per minute to $-25°C$, then rapidly to $-70°C$ or, eventually, $96°C$.

Thawing is achieved by immersion of the ampoule in a beaker containing water at $37 \pm 0.5°C$. It is, however, highly recommended to wear gloves and goggles while taking the ampoules out of the nitrogen and immersing them in water because ampoules sometimes explode. The contents of the ampoule are transferred under sterile conditions to a 25 cm^2 flask. After incubation of 4 to 5 hours at $37 \pm 0.5°C$ it is verified by microscopic observation that the cells are attached to the support. The liquid phase is then removed and replaced by some MEM containing 10% fetal calf serum. A new change of medium after 24 hours of incubation is necessary. As soon as a continuous cell layer is obtained, the culture can be subcultivated.

4.2. ANIMALS

Among laboratory animals only young mice (*Mus musculus*, var. *albinos*) can be utilized by a virology laboratory for water analysis. These animals permit the detection of Coxsackie viruses, for which certain types cannot be isolated on cell cultures. The sensitivity of newborn mice decreases rapidly with age. It is necessary to use mice aged at most 48 hours. Special care should be given to raising the animals by separating the males and the females and by programming the matings to obtain regular births, which are spread out over time. If such breeding proves to be difficult in the laboratory, it is possible to buy from specialized laboratories pregnant females ready to give birth. These are placed in cages or eventually in jars containing wood shavings for bedding. Water and nutritive granules should be provided regularly. The mothers are watched every day to ensure the immediate detection of the birth of young mice, which will be inoculated with samples within the first 24 hours (cf Chapter 5).

REFERENCES

Carrel, A. (1912) On the permanent life of tissues outside of the organism. *J. Exp. Med.* **15**, 516–528.

Dulbecco, R., and Vogt, M. (1954) Plaque formation and isolation of pure lines with poliomyelitis virus. *J. Exp. Med.* **99**, 167–182.

Eagle, H. (1959) Amino acid metabolism in mammalian cell cultures. *Science,* **130**, 432–437.

Eagle, H. (1955) Propagation in fluid medium of human epidermoid carcinoma, strain KB. *Proc. Soc. Exp. Biol.* **89**, 362–364.

Earle, W. R. (1943) Production of malignancy in vitro: Mouse fibroblast cultures and changes seen in living cells. *J. Nat. Cancer Inst.* **4**, 165–212.

Enders, J. F., Weller, T. H., and Robbins, F. C. (1949) Cultivation of the Lansing strain of poliomyelitis virus in cultures of various human embryonic tissues. *Science*, **109**, 85–87.

Hanks, J. H., and Wallace, R. E. (1949) Relation of oxygen and temperature in the preservation of tissues by refrigeration. *Proc. Soc. Exp. Biol.* **71**, 196–200.

Leibovitz, A. (1963) The growth and maintenance of tissue cultures in free gas exchange with the atmosphere. *Am. J. Hyg.* **78**, 173–180.

Moore, G. E., Gerner, R. E., and Franklin, H. A. (1967) Culture of normal human leukocytes. *JAMA*, **199**, 519–524.

Morgan, J. F., Morton, H. J., and Parker, R. C. (1950) Nutrition of animal cells in tissue culture: Initial studies on synthetic medium. *Proc. Soc. Exp. Biol.* **73**, 1–8.

Scherer, W. F., Syverton, J. T., and Gey, G. O. (1953) Studies on the propagation in vitro of poliomyelitis viruses. IV. Viral multiplication in a stable strain of human malignant epithelial cells (strain Hela) derived from an epidermoid carcinoma of the cervix. *J. Exp. Med.* **97**, 695–710.

Varani, J., Dame, M., and Beals, T. F. (1983) Growth of three established cell lines on glass microcarriers. *Biotechnol. Bioeng.* **25**, 1359–1372.

Chapter 5

ISOLATION TECHNIQUES

The process for the detection of viruses incorporates an isolation step, which is carried out by inoculation onto living cells (in vitro cell cultures or living animal). Cell lesions or pathological manifestations in the animal provide evidence for viral multiplication, thus signaling the presence of viruses in the inoculum.

5.1. ISOLATION ON CELL CULTURES

The cell cultures actually represent the simplest solution for the isolation of viruses. Even so, it is necessary to choose among all the cells that are available for culturing, bearing in mind the type of virus to be investigated. Likewise, it is essential to select an isolation technique either on a cell monolayer or on cells in suspension.

5.1.1. Choice of Cell Systems

All cells in culture do not present the same sensitivity to viruses. Depending on the cell systems and the viruses themselves, there is either a viral multiplication that is proven by the appearance of characteristic lesions (cytopathic effect) or a viral multiplication without any physical attack on the cells. A third possibility is, of course, the absence of any viral multiplication.

Most of the viruses that are regularly looked for in aqueous media can be isolated on diverse cellular systems whose susceptibility is indicated in Table 5.1.

The probability of isolating a virus from a sample increases with the number of cell systems that are inoculated. Increases in this number, however, become progressively more expensive for a laboratory. Nevertheless, it is desirable to carry out the isolations on several different cell systems.

5.1.2. Isolation on Integral Cellular Layers

Isolation on cell layers is carried out in two principal steps: inoculation of the sample with adsorption of the viruses on the cells, and incubation. The latter step is carried out in the presence of a liquid survival medium or in a gel medium.

5.1.2.1. In Liquid Medium

In liquid medium the multiplication of the virus in the interior of the cells leads to the liberation into the culture medium of newly formed virions. These particles are then capable of infecting any of the other cells in the layer, which often leads to its massive destruction.

Table 5.1. Sensitivity of different cell systems for isolating viruses

Cells	Virus	Polio-myelitic	Cocksackie A	Cocksackie B	Echo	Reovirus	Adenovirus
Primary	Monkey kidney (primary)	+	$-^a$	+	+	+	−
Established lines	Vero	+	$-^a$	+	+	+	±
	BGM	+	$-^a$	+	+	+	±
	HeLa	+	$-^a$	±	±	+	+
	KB	+	$-^a$	±	±	+	+
	Hep 2	+	$-^a$	+	±	+	+
	RD	+	$+^a$	−	+	±	±
	MRC$_5$	+	$+^a$	−	+	±	+*

^{a} With the exception of certain strains.

a. Inoculation. The first step is accomplished by means of the following series of procedures.

1. Select by microscopic examination the flasks that present continuous cell mono-layers.
2. Eliminate the culture medium by aspiration, using a sterile pipette.
3. Inoculate the sample on the cell layer in a ratio of 1 ml for every 25 cm² of culture.
4. Leave the inoculum in contact at 37°C for 1 hour while proceeding with a gentle stirring of the flasks every 10 minutes. During this period the viruses that might be present in the inoculum will fix themselves specifically to the cells.
5. Eliminate the inoculum by aspiration with a pipette, taking care not to damage the cell layer.
6. Add 2% calf serum MEM liquid in a ratio of 7 ml per 25 cm² of cell layer; then put into incubation.

Note that reference flasks, with cell cultures not receiving viral inoculum, are always prepared along with the test flasks.

b. Incubation and Observation. Incubation is carried out at 37°C. The appearance of the cell layer is observed every day with an inverse microscope to detect cell alterations and thus the cytopathic effect. The observation period lasts as long as the reference cells are in a good state, generally between 7 and 20 days. Viral multiplication is expressed by the appearance of a cytopathic effect and the progressive destruction of the cell layer (Chapter 6).

Because cytotoxic molecules can cause the same phenomenon, the viral nature of the destruction must be confirmed by a subculture and by an identification. Furthermore, even in the absence of any cellular alteration, a subculture is systematically carried out. It has been shown that the subculture increases the percentage of isolation by at least 20% (Foliguet et al, 1966).

c. Subculture. The preceding culture is submitted to three successive cycles of freezing and thawing, whereby the cells burst and liberate any viruses that have accumulated inside. A 10 minute centrifugation at 3000 *g* serves to eliminate cell debris, and the supernatant thus obtained is inoculated onto the integral cell layer using the procedures described above. Incubation proceeds at $37 \pm 0.5°C$.

Usually, any sample that shows a cytopathic effect is considered to be positive, since experience indicates that in nearly 99% of cases, a virus is really present. However, only final identification will permit confirmation of a positive case.

5.1.2.2. Agar Overlay (Plaque Method)

Like the preceding technique, the agar overlay method consists of inoculating the sample onto a cell culture. After the adsorption of viruses by the cells, the inoculum is eliminated and the cell layer is covered, this time by an agar medium. Under these conditions the viral particles multiply in the interior of the cells; because of the agar, however, the newly formed viruses cannot spread over the whole cell layer but can infect only the adjacent cells. The infection is thus propagated from neighbor to neighbor, and the multiplication of a particle is expressed by the apparition of a plaque or spot of circular cellular lysis, which is visible to the naked eye. The plaque appears as a colorless round zone, contrasting with the rest of the cell culture, which is colored with neutral red.

It must be noted that the plaque method is not applicable to the isolation of all viruses, for certain ones do not provoke the formation of plaques.

Two techniques can be recommended. One uses a medium containing a colorant (neutral red), which permits the formation of plaques to be observed, as indicated above. The other, using a medium without colorant, necessitates the fixing and staining of the cells before observation.

a. Vital Staining Technique. This approach has seven principal steps.

1. Inoculate 1 ml of the sample in a 25 cm² flask with a cell layer that has been cleared of the supernatant medium.f
2. Leave in contact for 2 hours at 22–25°C.
3. Eliminate the inoculum by aspiration with a pipette.
4. In presence of an inoculum that may be toxic, wash the cell layer by gentle stirring with a few milliliters of phosphate-buffered saline solution.
5. Cover the cell layer again with 7 ml of melted agar (45°C) medium containing neutral red (cf Chapter 4).
6. Let the agar solidify away from light.
7. Incubate the flasks, which have returned to 37°C, again away from light.

Control cell cultures not receiving viral inoculum are always prepared simultaneously.

Observations are carried out with the naked eye, and the plaques are numbered every second day for 6 to 14 days. The duration of the period for reading depends on the state of conservation of the control cells, which have been cultivated under the same agar medium.

Certain lysis plaques can be provoked by the presence of toxic molecules. It is thus necessary to carry out a subculture of each one to verify that they have indeed been provoked by a virus, and to obtain a liquid sample with the aim of precisely identifying the virus. Such a subculture is carried out with a sterile pipette slightly bent at one end. At the center of the target plaque, a fragment of agar and of subjacent cellular layer is aspirated and immediately inoculated onto a new cell culture containing the liquid medium. The culture thus seeded is put into incubation at 37°C and the cell layer is submitted to daily microscopic observation. The presence of the cytopathic effect confirms the viral origin of the lysis plaque.

The resulting viral suspension theoretically corresponds to a pure viral population stemming from the development of the unique viral particle that generated the plaque. Later, this viral population will permit the precise identification of the virus concerned (Chapter 6). In principle, each plaque should be confirmed by subculture, since Leong et al (1978) have shown that 30 to 40% did not yield an isolated virus. In practice, systematic subculture is an extremely costly and time-consuming procedure, and only 10 to 50% of randomly chosen plaques are thus tested.

The vital staining technique can also be carried out in petri dishes under conditions of incubation in an atmosphere richfin carbon dioxide.

b. Technique Without Vital Staining. Onto a 60 mm diameter plastic petri dish with cell monolayer culture, introduce 1 ml of the suspension to be tested. Then perform the following steps.

1. Let the viruses be absorbed by contact for 2 hours at 22–25°C.
2. Eliminate the inoculum by aspiration with a pipette.
3. In the presence of an inoculum that may be toxic, wash the cell layer by gentle stirring with several milliliters of phosphate-buffered saline solution.
4. Again, cover the cells with 45°C melted agar medium (cf Chapter 4).
5. Let the material solidify.
6. Incubate the dishes, which have been returned to 37°C, in a carbon dioxide incubator.

After incubation for 3 to 7 days, and fixation and elimination of the agar, the lysis plaques are revealed by a staining applied according to the following procedure.

1. Fix the cell layer by adding 4 ml of trichloroacetic acid at 10% for 30 minutes.
2. Eliminate the agar layer.
3. Stain the cell layer that is attached to the bottom of the petri dish with 2 ml of a 0.15% crystal violet solution for 15 minutes.
4. Wash with distilled water; observe and count the nonstained plaques on a violet background layer (Fig. 5.1).

This simple technique presents the major inconvenience of not allowing for subculture, since the viruses are destroyed during fixation.

Consequently, it is impossible on the one hand to verify that the plaques have a viral origin and on the other to identify the isolated viruses.

All the operations for the isolation of the viruses on a cell monolayer are summarized in Figure 5.2.

5.1.3. Isolation Using a Cell Suspension

Isolation using a cell suspension considerably increases the sensitivity of the method for the detection of viruses (Cooper, 1967). This method is extended over two phases.

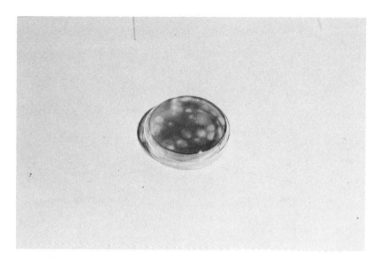

Figure 5.1. Plaques of cellular lysis after staining with crystal violet.

First, the inoculum is introduced into a suspension of cells in growth medium. Any viral particles that are present will be fixed on the cells. Second, a liquid or agar nutritive medium is added to the mixture. Then the mixture is incubated at 37°C.

In a liquid medium the cells form a sediment and attach themselves to the support. In the absence of viruses, they will multiply and form a cell layer. Conversely, in the presence of virus, the cells will be destroyed.

In agar medium the cells remain dispersed in the medium, and the viral multiplication is detected by the appearance of clear zones of lysis.

5.1.3.1. In Liquid Medium

a. Inoculation. The procedure is as follows.

1. Prepare a suspension of cells in growth medium in a ratio of 3×10^5 cells per milliliter. Mix the sample to be analyzed with this suspension in a ratio of 1:2.
2. Homogenize, then gently stir for 15 minutes at $37 \pm 0.5°C$.
3. Spread the sample-cell mixture onto sterile vessels and let incubate.

b. Incubation and Observation. Incubation is carried out at $37 \pm 0.5°C$. The observation period lasts as long as the control cells are in good condition, that is, generally for 7 to 20 days. Daily microscopic examination allows one to observe first the presence or absence of a cell layer in formation and eventually, after several days of incubation, any alterations of the cell layer.

The failure to form a cell layer or the alteration of such a layer indicates cell destruction; however, the viral origin of this phenomenon should always be confirmed by subculture, followed by identification (cf Chapter 6).

c. Subculture. When using a cell suspension in a liquid medium, subcultures are carried out according to the same procedures used in connection with the analogous technique for integral cell layer described in Section 5.1.2.1.c.

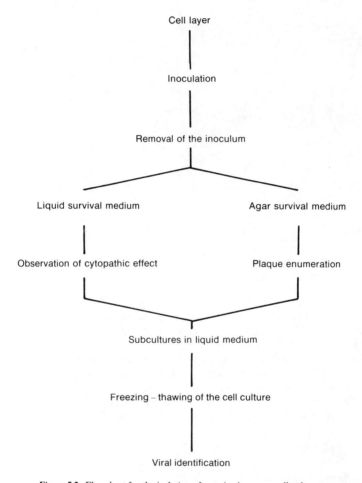

Figure 5.2. Flowchart for the isolation of enteric viruses on cell cultures.

5.1.3.2. In Agar Medium

a. Inoculation. The procedure is as follows.

1. Prepare a suspension of cells in survival medium in a ratio of 10^7 cells per milliliter.
2. Mix the sample to be analyzed with this suspension in a ratio of 1:2.
3. Stir for 15 minutes at $37 \pm 0.5°C$.
4. Add 10 ml of 45°C melted agar medium (cf Section 5.1.2.1.a).
5. After rapid homogenization, pour the mixture into a plastic flask.

b. Incubation and Observation. The incubation is carried out at $37 \pm 0.5°C$. The observation period lasts as long as the reference cells (ie, nonseeded) remain in good

Table 5.2. Comparison of the inoculation methods in liquid or agar media

Inoculation	Advantages	Inconveniences
In liquid medium	Rare toxicity Possibility of blind (ie, without cytopathic effect) subcultures Greater sensitivity Easy subcultures	No separation of the different types of virus With a mixture of viruses with slow and high replication kinetics, the slower ones cannot be isolated
Under agar medium	Separation of the viruses (rarer mixing)	Frequent toxicity Subcultures impossible without cytopathic effect Difficult subcultures No detection of viruses that do not form lysis plaques

condition. The presence of virus causes the formation of spherical and uncolored lysis plaques in the middle of the agar medium, which is colored pink by neutral red.

Certain lysis plaques can be provoked by the presence of toxic molecules. Therefore each plaque must be subcultured to verify that it has been provoked by a virus and to obtain a liquid sample for the purpose of precisely identifying the virus.

c. Subculture. The procedures are identical to those described in Section 5.1.2.2.a, for agar overlay.

5.1.4. Limitations of the Isolation Techniques on Cell Cultures

The different methods discussed thus far have advantages as well as some inconveniences. These are summarized in Table 5.2.

5.2. ISOLATION BY INOCULATION OF MICE

Coxsackie A and B viruses present in water samples can be detected following inoculation of newborn mice. In young mice these viruses provoke diseases whose symptoms and lesions vary according to the virus type that is inoculated. After inoculation, the development of the young mice must be observed regularly, to permit the investigator to record the characteristic clinical manifestations.

5.2.1. Inoculation

The decontaminated sample is inoculated into a litter of mice less than 48 hours old. The litters are chosen in such a way that at least five animals are inoculated. The young mice are left with the mothers either in glass jars or in cages. The inoculation is done intracerebrally or intraperitonally.

By the intracerebral route, the inoculation is done with a 1 ml syringe graduated to tenths of a milliliter. A volume of 0.10 ml is injected subcutaneously in the cervical region, producing a papule 2 mm in diameter under the skin. The needle is thenfdriven into the brain without pushing on the piston of the syringe, to ensure against the provoking of lesions by pressure. This technique allows one to partially limit the rate of mortality due solely to inoculation trauma.

By the intraperitonal route, the volume of inoculum injected is 0.10 ml.

Once inoculated, the mice are returned to the maternal nest.

5.2.2. Observation

The animals are regularly observed each day for a period of 14 days. The mice that die before the second day are eliminated and the cause of death is imputed to the trauma of injection by the intracerebral route. The clinical manifestations that are observed vary according to the virus responsible. In the case of a Coxsackie A virus the mice are often apathetic and cyanosed. They present a limplike paralysis starting in the posterior extremities, then progressing toward the cephalic pole.

In the case of a Coxsackie B virus the animal presents signs of ill-regulated agitation, then spastic paralytic phenomena, particularly in the posterior membranes, with ataxia and uncoordination of movements. The mice turn in circles, and when put on their backs they cannot turn over. The symptomatology of infection by Coxsackie B virus can, however, be less pronounced and can be characterized uniquely by a state of progressive denutrition leading to cachexis.

With the appearance of paralysis or spastic movements in one or several animals, the litter is watched two or three times a day, since the mothers will eat their young as soon as they become sick. When the spastic or paralytic symptoms reach a maximum intensity the mice are taken out of the nest and examined, then sacrificed and put into two groups. The first group is used for histological examination. The second serves for immunological identification.

REFERENCES

Berg, G., Safferman, R. S., Dahling, D. R., Berman, D., and Hurst, C. Y. (1984) "U.S. Environmental Protection Agency Manual of Methods for Virology." Publication EPA-600/4-84-013, E.P.A, Cincinnati, OH.

Cooper, P. D. (1967) The plaque assay of animal viruses. *Adv. Virus Res.* **8**, 319–378.

Foliguet, J. M., Schwartzbrod, L., and Gaudin, O. G. (1966) La pollution virale des eaux usees de surface et d'alimentation. *Bull. Organ. Mond. Sante*, **35**, 737–749.

Leong, L. Y. C., Barrett, S. J., and Trussel, R. R. (1978) False positives in testing of secondary sewage for enteric viruses. Abstract, 78th Meeting of the American Society for Microbiology.

Chapter 6

IDENTIFICATION TECHNIQUES

The isolation of the agent responsible for the destruction of cell cultures or for pathological manifestations in the animal is only the first step in a virological analysis. Next, it is essential to identify this agent precisely.

6.1. IDENTIFICATION OF VIRUSES PROVOKING A CYTOPATHIC EFFECT ON CELL CULTURES

The identification of viruses isolated on cell cultures is a multistep procedure. First, observation of the cytopathic effect confirms that the agent isolated is indeed a virus, and it establishes a way of diagnosis by classification within a family of viruses. Second, implementing immunological reactions permits the precise identification of the virus that has been isolated. Finally, and for poliomyelitic viruses only, experiments for intratype differentiation are put into operation to differentiate between wild and vaccinal strains.

6.1.1. PRELIMINARY DIAGNOSIS

Preliminary diagnosis consists of observation of the cytopathic effect. This is done by examination of the infected cell cultures, either directly or after fixation and staining of the cells.

6.1.1.1. Direct Observation of Cells

a. In Liquid Medium. The infected primary cultures or subcultures are examined by inverse microscopy in parallel with the control cells, which were cultivated under the same conditions. This differentiates the cytological modifications provoked by the viral multiplication from those due to external causes (spontaneous degeneration of the cells, fungal or bacterial contamination, etc).

Not only is the nature of the cytopathic effect determined, but also its delay in appearing. This depends on the group of the virus concerned and on the quantity of viral particles inoculated.

Poliomyelitic viruses provoke a cellular degeneration that in general appears very rapidly. After 24 to 48 hours round, refringent, and refracted cells are observed, and some of them are detached from the vessel walls. Between 48 and 72 hours the cell layer is completely destroyed and the dead cells float in the nutritive medium. Some other members of the family of enteroviruses (ECHO virus, Coxsackie B virus) provoke the same type of cytopathic effect, but the lesions in the cell layer often appear later and in a less massive way; the percentage of cells attacked can vary from 20 to 90%.

The reoviruses cause alterations in the cell layer that are similar to those due to enteroviruses; however, they arrive generally much later (ie, in 6–7 days). They are clearly less massive and less characteristic. Besides, the cells attacked show no evidence of refringence.

According to the density of adenoviruses present in the inoculum, there can be two types of cell layer destruction. If the inoculum is rich, 2 to 3 hours after inoculation one observes a retraction of the cell layer and its partial detachment from the vessel wall. This phenomenon is provoked directly by the action of a protein from the adenovirus, namely the cell detaching factor, and it has no direct relation to viral multiplication. The actual cytopathic effect happens 5 to 6 days later and is characterized by the presence of small centers of cellular destruction in which the cells become refringent and tend to detach themselves from the glass. Furthermore, there often exists a cytoplasmic retraction, which makes the cell layer resemble lacework.

b. Agar Overlay. The cultures under agar are observed with the naked eye. The zones of cellular lysis appear round, translucent, and whitish, contrasting with the rest of the cell culture, which is stained pink. Their aspect varies as a function of the virus responsible.

As for the enteroviruses, it is found that poliomyelitic viruses provoke the appearance of round plaques with well-defined limits and clear centers. Generally, they appear rapidly (2–3 days), but it is not rare to see them appear much later. The Coxsackie A_9 and B_1 to B_5 viruses give plaques whose edges are poorly defined. The delay in appearance is generally longer than for poliomyelitic viruses. The ECHO viruses provoke plaques whose morphology is quite variable according to the type implicated. Generally, they are observed 4 to 12 days after incubation.

c. After Fixation and Staining of the Cells. Staining the cells that have shown a viral infection permits a better investigation by direct examination and a more precise description of the cell lesions. This operation is carried out on cell cultures in a Leighton tube (cf Chapter 4) after the viral suspension to be identified has been inoculated. During incubation at $37 \pm 0.5°C$, regular microscopic observations are performed and on appearance of the first lesions one proceeds to fixation, then to the staining of the cells, according to the following protocol.

1. Eliminate the culture medium and replace it with Bouin fixating liquid (Jaulmes et al, 1958).
2. After 60 minutes contact, discard the fixating liquid and replace it with 70% alcohol, which is saturated with lithium carbonate (to wash away the picric acid and remove the color of the preparation).
3. Rinse with distilled water then stain for 15 minutes with Man's acid hemalum solution (Cateigne and Maurin, 1965).
4. Put the preparation in contact for about 5 seconds with acidic alcohol (1% HCl in 70% alcohol), then for several seconds with alkaline water.
5. Add to the slide a 0.5% aqueous eosin solution and leave in contact for 1 minute.
6. Rinse with water and dry the preparation by successive washings in 70 and 90% alcohol followed by absolute ethanol.

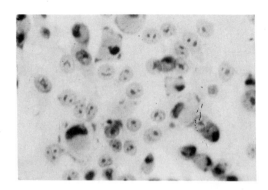

Figure 6.1. Cytopathic effect provoked by a poliomyelitic virus (KB cells).

7. Keep the slide in toluene for 5 minutes; then with the aid of Canada balsam attach it to the slide holder.
8. Observe under the microscope: the cytoplasm is rose colored, the nucleus is blue-violet, and the nucleoli are red.

The lesions observed vary according to the genus to which the viruses responsible belong. For example, enterovirus-infected cells show characteristic lesions. They comprise a large eosinophilic cytoplasmic inclusion, which pushes the pycnotic cellular nucleus to the periphery, often showing the form of a crescent. In general, it is possible to observe infected and normal cells on the same slide at the same time (Fig. 6.1).

Reoviruses provoke the formation of either a voluminous, eosinophic cytoplasmic inclusion that circles the nucleus, or of small, rounded intracytoplasmic inclusions, which are often grouped around the nucleus. In any case, the nucleus is left alone and is not deformed (Fig. 6.2).

Adenovirus-caused lesions are localized essentially in the region of the nucleus. They are made up of inclusions, which surround the nucleoli. During the first stages of infection the inclusions are multiple and eosinophilic. Later they are grouped into a basophilic central mass. The peripheral part of the nucleus is homogeneous or

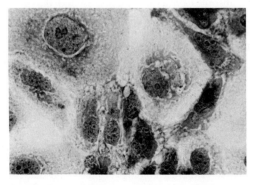

Figure 6.2. Cytopathic effect provoked by a reovirus (BSC cells).

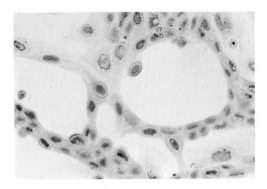

Figure 6.3. Cytopathic effect provoked by a type 7 adenovirus (primary cells from a monkey kidney).

sprinkled with vacuoles, which are in fact artifacts of the fixation, albeit very useful for diagnosis. Whatever stage the lesions are in, the nucleoli are always left alone (Fig. 6.3).

6.1.2. Immunological Identification by Neutralization

Only immunological testing can confirm the preliminary diagnosis and affirm the precise identity of the viruses that have been isolated. All immunological tests use an in vitro antigen–antibody reaction. Viruses are antigenic, as indeed are all microorganisms. That is, they contain antigens that are capable of reacting specifically with corresponding antibodies by forming an antigen–antibody (Ag–Ab) complex in which the virus can no longer express its properties and its biological activities. For the identification of viruses, the most widely used reaction is that of neutralization of the cytopathic effect.

6.1.2.1. Principle

Whenever a virus is put in the presence of specific antibodies, the antibodies will combine selectively with the antigens present on the surface of the virus. Consequently, the virus cannot be absorbed on a susceptible cell and thus is incapable of being a parasite, of multiplying and provoking a cytopathic effect. Thus, the virus is effectively neutralized.

This neutralization reaction (Fig. 6.4) is carried out in two steps. In the first or immunological reaction step, the unknown virus is put into contact with known antibodies (serum). If the virus corresponds to the antibodies, it is neutralized by the antigen–antibody reaction. If, on the other hand, it does not correspond to the antibodies, it remains free. Neutralization is not revealed by a visible phenomenon, however, and thus a second step is called for.

In the second or disclosure reaction step, the product of the immunological reaction is inoculated into a system (eg, cell cultures) that can reveal the virus in question.

The manifestation of a cytopathic effect signifies that the virus has not been neutralized in the course of the immunological phase and that it does not correspond to the antibodies chosen.

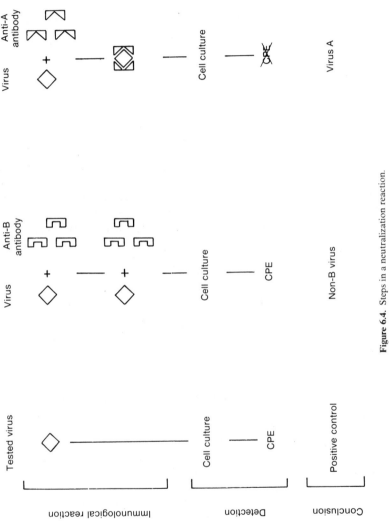

Figure 6.4. Steps in a neutralization reaction.

If, on the contrary, the cell culture remains intact, the absence of viral multiplication is indicated; that is, neutralization did occur. The noted antibodies put into reaction match the virus, which then is identified.

6.1.2.2. Procedures

The identification of poliomyelitic viruses is taken as an example, but the method can be used for the other viruses that are isolated from water. The technique calls for known mixtures of antipoliomyelitic sera and monkey kidney cells cultivated on microplates (other vessels and other cells can be used). It is carried out in several steps.

a. Dilution of the Sera. The identification of poliomyelitic viruses calls for three sera containing antibodies: type 1, type 2, and type 3 (these sera of known titer are distributed by several firms). They are diluted in the culture medium in such a way as to yield mixtures of antibodies (anti 1 + 2, anti 2 + 3, anti 3 + 1, and anti 1 + 2 + 3). In all cases the dilutions are conducted to ensure the use of at least 1600 neutralizing units of each antibody per milliliter.

b. Viral Suspensions. It is necessary to proceed initially with the titration of the suspension of the virus to be identified (cf Chapter 7). The dilutions are calculated as a function of the titer obtained, to ensure that the resulting suspension contains a 50% cytopathic dose of around 4000 CPD_{50} per milliliter (see Chapter 7: Section 7.3.1).

c. Neutralization. This can be done directly on a sterile microplate, and the results displayed according to the scheme in Figure 6.5. The distribution may be as follows:

In each of the 16 wells corresponding to a mixture of serum, 25 μl of the antibody mixture

In each of the 10 wells corresponding to a virus, 25 μl of titrated viral suspension

In each of the 16 control cell wells, 50 μl of culture medium

In each of the 8 reference serum wells and the 16 reference virus wells, 25 μl of culture medium

The plate is covered, the mixtures are gently agitated, and then incubation in a CO_2-enriched atmosphere occurs, at $37 \pm 0.5°C$.

d. Disclosure. After 3 hours of incubation, the following steps are performed

1. Spread in each of the wells 50 μl of the growth medium, containing 400,000 monkey kidney cells per milliliter.
2. Incubate the closed plate under the same conditions as before.
3. Observe each well under the inverse microscope after 3 and 5 days of incubation.

The control cell cultures with and without sera should present a continuous cell layer. The reference virus wells will be characterized by the absence of a cell layer (cellular destruction). Types 1, 2, and 3 poliomyelitic virus should be neutralized by the corresponding sera (wells with a continuous cell layer and no cytopathic effect). The other wells may or may not show cellular destruction. Thus the results can be interpreted from the overall set of observations. Figure 6.6 gives an example of some results.

Although the neutralization technique is by far the most widely used, the inhibition of the hemagglutination reaction is still valuable for identifying certain viruses (eg, reovirus and adenovirus). This technique is not described here. Any isolated strain can

Antipoliomylitic Sera

anti 1 + 2		anti 2 + 3		anti 3 + 1		anti 1 + 2 + 3		Virus control		Cell control		
												Virus A
												Virus B
												Virus C
												Virus D
												Polio virus 1
												Polio virus 2
												Polio virus 3
												Reference sera

Figure 6.5. Scheme for interpreting a neutralization reaction carried out on a microplate.

Antipoliomylitic Sera

1 + 2		2 + 3		3 + 1		1 + 2 + 3		Virus control		Cell control		
0	0	0	0	+	+	0	0	+	+	0	0	Virus A
0	0	+	+	0	0	0	0	+	+	0	0	Virus B
+	+	+	+	0	0	0	0	+	+	0	0	Virus C
+	+	+	+	+	+	+	+	+	+	0	0	Virus D
0	0	+	+	0	0	0	0	+	+	0	0	Polio virus 1
0	0	0	0	+	+	0	0	+	+	0	0	Polio virus 2
+	+	0	0	0	0	0	0	+	+	0	0	Polio virus 3
0	0	0	0	0	0	0	0			0	0	Reference sera

Figure 6.6. Reading of a microplate neutralization reaction for the identification of poliomyelitic viruses: + = CPE and 0 = absence of a CPE. From these data it can be concluded that sample A contains a type 2 poliomyelitic virus, sample B contains a type 1 poliomyelitic virus, sample C contains a mixture of types 1 and 3 poliomyelitic virus, and sample D contains a non-poliomyelitic virus.

be sent to a national reference center for identification or confirmation of identification.

6.1.3. Intratypic Differentiation of Poliomyelitic Viruses

Since the introduction of oral antipoliomyelitic vaccination with live, attenuated virus (Sabin strain), it is more and more frequent to find vaccinal-type poliomyelitic viruses in the aqueous medium. It is particularly important to be able to make the distinction between the wild, pathogenic strains and the so-called attenuated ones. Numerous tests, called in vitro intratypic differentiations, have been described (eg, d, A, Aa, E, rct40 markers). Some immunological tests have also been proposed. The neutralization technique due to MacBride (1959) has been abandoned for routine tests because it is costly and timeconsuming and requires the use of specific rabbit sera, which are difficult to prepare, from vaccinal and wild strains.

Van Wezel and Hazendonk (1979) have proposed a neutralization test using sera rendered specific for vaccinal and wild strains by adsorption on an enormous quantity of concentrated and purified heterospecific poliomyelitic virus. This preparation of sera is extremely costly, and the results obtained have shown a good agreement with the data for thermal rct40 marker.

A genetic characterization (oligonucleotide map using restriction enzymes) of wild and vaccinal strains has been described by Nottay et al (1980).

Couillin et al (1982) have obtained several lines of hybridomas that secrete mono-clonal antibodies neutralizing type 1 poliomyelitic virus. Certain lines are specific for the Mahoney prototype wild strain and others for the LSc–2ab vaccinal strain.

The use of monoclonal antibodies represents an advance in the intratypic differen-tiation of poliomyelitic viruses. The results obtained reveal very good agreement with the tests of serodifferentiation using sera prepared by cross-adsorption, according to Van Wezel and Hazendonk (1979).

The thermal marker rct40 has been the one most frequently selected for many years; however, its value for intratypic differentiation has been contested, in particular by certain American authors, and generally it is being supplanted by neutralization tests using monoclonal antibodies.

6.1.3.1. Intratypic Differentiation by the Thermal rct40 Marker Test

a. Principle. This test relies on the fact that wild strains of poliomyelitic virus multiply on cell cultures at 40°C while attenuated strains do so very poorly or not al all (Lwoff and Lwoff, 1959). The proof consists in titrating the virus in parallel at 37 and 40°C, then comparing the titers obtained for each incubation temperature.

b. Procedures. The technique described here is carried out with the primary cells of monkey kidney, and the test is performed on microplates with 96 wells. However, other vessels also can be used.

Each test involves plates, which will be treated in the same way, but one is put in incubation at 37°C and the other at 40°C. The results from each plate will be recorded as shown in Figure 6.7.

Dilutions of each viral suspension (including reference strains) are made from 10^{-1} to 10^{-8} in culture medium, which is distributed as follows:

> In each well, 50 µl of cell suspension of monkey kidney containing 400,000 cells per milliliter in a growth medium
>
> In each of the reference cell wells, 100 µl of culture medium
>
> In each of all the other wells, 50 µl of culture medium
>
> For each virus in two wells by dilution, 50 µl of the corresponding dilution

Each plate is then covered put into a plastic bag, which is heat-sealed. One plate is incubated at 37.0 ± 0.1°C, the other at 40.0 ± 0.1°C for 5 days. This incubation is

Viral dilutions	Virus A	Virus B	Virus C	Reference strains		Cell control
				Wild strain	Vaccinal strain	
10^{-1}						
10^{-2}						
10^{-3}						
10^{-4}						
10^{-5}						
10^{-6}						
10^{-7}						
10^{-8}						

Figure 6.7. Scheme for recording data from an rct40 test carried out on a microplate.

carried out in perfectly controlled water baths. The plates should in no case be taken out during the incubation period.

c. Results. The control cell culture should present an intact cell layer. The titer of each viral suspension is determined for the two incubation temperatures from the number of wells presenting a cytopathic effect (cf Chapter 7).

The reference wild strain and the other wild strains are rct40 + if the difference between the titers at 37 and at 40°C is less than or equal to 1 log. The reference vaccinal strain and the other vaccinal strains are rct40 − if their titer at 40°C is less than at least 4 log of their titer at 37°C.

Thus, by this technique, it is possible to accomplish an intratypic differentiation of these poliomyelitic viruses for neuropathogenic wild strains and for nonpathogenic vaccinal or attenuated strains.

6.1.3.2. Intratypic Differentiation by Neutralization with Monoclonal Antibodies

a. Principle. The test is founded on the seroneutralization of the strains to be typed by specific monoclonal antibodies of vaccinal or wild strains. The experiment consists of carrying out the titration of the viral suspension to be typed in the absence or presence of monoclonal antibodies and then deducing the neutralization index.

b. Procedures. The three types of monoclonal antibody used in this test are: anti-vaccinal Sabin "S" strain, anti-wild "W" strain, and anti-constant character "K."

The hybridoma supernatants are titrated beforehand to determine the dilution that permits intratypic differentiation (largest dilution of anti-Sabin antibodies that completely neutralizes the Sabin strain without neutralizing the wild strain). This dilution varies from 1/10 to 1/50 according to the monoclonal antibody.

Logarithmic dilutions (10^{-1}–10^{-8}) of each viral suspension to test are carried out in basal Eagle's medium without serum.

Using Figure 6.8 as a guide, a microtitration plate with 96 wells for cell cultures is filled (25 μl per well) and treated according to the following protocol:

In columns 1 and 2: BEM without serum

In columns 3 and 4: anti-Sabin monoclonal

In columns 5 and 6: anti-wild monoclonal

In columns 7 and 8: anti-constant monoclonal

In lines AH: the viral dilutions 10^{-1} to 10^{-8}

Control cell cultures with and without the monoclonal references are prepared, stirred, covered, and left in contact for 2 hours at 37°C in a CO_2 incubator.

Distribution is in a ratio of 50 μl per well of a suspension of BGM to 4×10^5 cells per milliliter in BEM + 6% fetal calf serum. Incubation proceeds for 3 days in a CO_2 incubator at 37°C, followed by microscopic observation.

c. Results. The reference antibodies and cells should show an intact cell layer, observation of the wells in columns 1 and 2 will allow one to determine the titer of the viral suspension, and microscopic observation of the wells of the other columns the titer of the viral suspension in the presence of the different monoclonal antibodies.

The neutralization index is then determined by calculating the difference between the viral titers (in log) in the presence and absence of the monoclonal antibodies. It should be 3 or greater.

Viral dilutions	Virus		anti-S antibody +virus		anti-W antibody +virus		anti-K antibody +virus				Control		
	1	2	3	4	5	6	7	8	9	10	11	12	
10^{-1} A	+	+	+	+	+	+	+	+			−	−	anti-S antibody
10^{-2} B	+	+	+	−	+	+	+	+			−	−	
10^{-3} C	+	+	−	−	+	+	−	−			−	−	anti-W antibody
10^{-4} D	+	+	−	−	+	+	−	−			−	−	
10^{-5} E	+	+	−	−	+	+	−	−			−	−	anti-K antibody
10^{-6} F	−	+	−	−	−	−	−	−			−	−	
10^{-7} G	−	+	−	−	−	−	−	−			−	−	
10^{-8} H	−	−	−	−	−	−	−	−			−	−	Cell control
Titre	$10^{6.5}$		10^{2}		$10^{5.5}$		$10^{2.5}$						

Figure 6.8. Results of a neutralization reaction on a microplate for the intratypic differentiation of a type 1 poliomyelitic virus.

The example given in Figure 6.8 would be interpreted as follows: The neutralization index is

4.5 with anti-Sabin "S" antibody

1 with anti-wild "W" antibody

4 with anti-constant character "K" antibody

Thus, with this technique, it is possible to accomplish intratypic differentiation of the wild and vaccinal types of poliomyelitic virus.

6.2. IDENTIFICATION OF THE VIRUSES MULTIPLYING ON CELL CULTURES WITHOUT PROVOKING A CYTOPATHIC EFFECT

A certain number of viruses encountered in water cannot be isolated on cell cultures because they do not provoke a cytopathic effect. Some of these viruses (eg, the rotaviruses) can rapidly multiply in the cells; others (eg, the hepatitis A virus: Crance et al, 1983) show intracellular multiplication only after a very long incubation (6–10 weeks). There are even some that do not exhibit in vitro multiplication in cells that can be detected by present technology, as is the case for the Norwalk virus and related viruses.

Although at present the routine detection of hepatitis A virus in cell cultures is not conceivable and remains in the domain of basic research, this is not the case for the detection of rotaviruses in water (Smith and Gerba, 1982; Deetz et al, 1984; Gerba et al, 1984).

6.2.1. Detection of Rotaviruses

6.2.1.1. Principle

The detection and quantification of rotaviruses from water concentrates is founded on a technique linking the in vitro culture on cells and demonstrating of viral multiplication by an immunofluorescence reaction, which permits visualization of the rotavirus infected cells. An antigen detectable by fluorescence is synthesized in 24 hours in the cytoplasm of the infected cell.

6.2.1.2. Procedures

Some MA 104 cell monolayers are grown at $37 \pm 0.5°C$ in multiple boxes with six wells each. Then 0.50 ml of concentrate or of viral suspension is inoculated in each of the wells. The boxes are put into incubation at $37 \pm 0.5°C$ for 15 minutes, then 0.03 ml of a 1/60 dilution of pancreatine and 0.20 ml of the growth medium are added. The boxes are then centrifuged at 200 g for 1 hour at $23°C$.

The medium floating above the cell layers after centrifugation is eliminated, and one proceeds to a washing of the layers with several milliliters of a phosphate-buffered saline solution.

The cells are then covered again with 2 ml of growth medium and incubated for 48 hours at $37 \pm 0.5°C$ in a CO_2 incubator. After the incubation period the medium is eliminated, the cell layers are washed with a few milliliters of a phosphate-buffered saline solution, then fixed by methanol at 4°C for 5 minutes and dried in the open air.

Before staining, the cell monolayers are rehydrated by addition of phosphate-buffered saline solution for 5 minutes. They are treated with 25 μl of antirotavirus SA 11 guinea pig serum; then, after washing with a few milliliters of phosphate-buffered saline solution, they are stained with goat serum containing guinea pig anti-immunoglobulin bound to fluorescein isothiocyanate.

After washing and drying of the cell layers, fluorescence microscopy is conducted, and the points (foci) of fluorescence are found and quantified.

6.3. IDENTIFICATION OF VIRUSES ISOLATED FROM NEWBORN MICE

The observation of clinical manifestations that appear after the inoculation of animals (cf Chapter 5) allows preliminary diagnosis of a Coxsackie A or B virus. The identification is arrived at first through histological examination of the tissues of the animal and then by immunological tests.

6.3.1. Histological Examination

The first group of dead or sacrificed baby mice is immersed in Bouin's liquid. The animals are then put into paraffin for sectioning and thin slices are obtained with a microtome. After hot fixation on a slide, the slices are stained according to classical techniques in histology. Microscopic examination of these slices generally allows the investigator to distinguish between infections provoked by Coxsackie viruses of groups A and B.

6.3.1.1. Coxsackie A Virus

In animals infected by the Coxsackie A virus there exists a characteristic alteration of the striated muscles, principally the skeletal muscles, consisting of a generalized myopathy infwhich all the signs of degeneration of the muscular fiber can be observed. The fibers that are first attacked inflate together, lose their longitudinal and transversal striation, and fragment at the same time as they hyalinize and take on a homogeneous aspect. A regenerative activity with hypertrophy and multiplication of the nuclei of the intact sarcolemma can be observed at the border between the dead tissue and the part not destroyed. One can also note a substantial inflammatory reaction in the interstitial tissue.

6.3.1.2. Coxsackie B Virus

The lesions formed in the young mouse by the Coxsackie B viruses are at the same time more numerous, more polymorphic, and different than those provoked by the group A viruses.

The major characteristic of infection by a Coxsackie B virus is an attack on the central nervous system, especially a more or less pronounced necrosis of the encephalon. These neurotropic lesions are not limited to the cerebral hemispheres and cerebellum but can attack the medulla and different rachidian ganglions, where they cause necrosis of the neurons.

These particular histological manifestations can be accompanied by other lesions in tissues, muscles, fat, pancreas, liver, or glands, according to the case. Muscular lesions can affect the striated muscles, but in localized zones, primarily in the intercostal region and in the diaphragm. In some cases, centers of necrosis spread to the myocardium. In the region of the subscapular brown fat, a major necrosis occurs.

These diverse lesions are specific enough by themselves to distinguish between the two groups of Coxsackie virus. However, the immunological tests alone permit precise identification of the type.

6.4. IDENTIFICATION WITHOUT INOCULATION INTO SUSCEPTIBLE SYSTEMS

Paralleling the classical techniques for the isolation of viruses in cell cultures or in animals, other methods exist for the detection and identification of viruses. All share an immunological basis, but we single out radioimmunology, electron microscopy and immunomicroscopy, passive hemagglutination (the SPACE test: see Section 6.4.2), and immunoenzymology. We will not discuss the radioimmunological methods, which are in the domain of specialized laboratories.

6.4.1. Electron Microscopy and Immunomicroscopic Methods

Electron immunomicroscopy consists of putting the sample to be analyzed into contact with an immune serum containing antibodies directed specifically against the sought-after virus. If this virus is present in the sample, there will be a virus–antibody combination. The existence of such an antigen–antibody complex is revealed by observation with an electron microscope. One then ascertains the presence of aggregates made of virus bound by the corresponding antibodies.

The electron microscope can be used alone for the detection of viruses whose morphology is sufficiently characteristic (eg, rotavirus).

6.4.2. The SPACE Test

The test for solid phase aggregation of coupled erythrocytes, SPACE, is carried out in two steps. In the immunological step, antibodies directed against the virus in question are attached to the wells of microplates. The sample to be analyzed is then added and put in incubation. During this phase any virus that is present in the sample will combine with the antibodies in the well and form an antigen–antibody complex. After elimination of the sample, the material remaining in each well will be the viruses fixed to the antibodies.

In the second or disclosure step, erythrocytes that are combined with antibodies identical to those attached to the wells are added to the wells. These antibodies in turn will combine with anya viruses that might be are fixed in the well and will form a new antigen–antibody complex, which is visualized by the adherence of the erythrocytes to the sides of the wells.

This technique, recommended by Bradburne et al (1979), can be used for the detection of rotaviruses in stool.

6.4.3. Immunoenzymological Methods

The originality of the immunoenzymological techniques lies in the marker, an enzyme that indicates the reaction. Many methods have been proposed (Guesdon and Avrameas, 1979).

6.4.3.1. Principle

The most widely used method in virology is the enzymelinked immunosorbent assay, or ELISA technique. During the first phase of this technique the antibody (Ab) that is specific for the desired virus is trapped on a solid support. The test sample is brought into contact with this support, and if the virus infquestion is present, it will combine with the attached antibodies. This antigen–antibody complex (Ag–Ab) is invisible, and a disclosure step is necessary.

The disclosure can be done according to either of two different protocols: the single-sandwich or the double sandwich technique.

In the single-sandwich method, specific antibodies marked by an enzyme are added. These marked antibodies combine by way of the antibodies with the viruses that are attached to the support. When the substrate that is specific for the enzyme is added, it is attacked by the enzyme, as revealed by a color change.

The double-sandwich method begins with the addition of the antibodies specific for the virus in question but of a different origin (eg, rabbit instead of guinea pig). These antibodies fix themselves onto the virusantibody complex. After elimination of the noncombined antibodies, the investigator adds anti-immunoglobulin antibodies for the previously used species, marked by an enzyme (*). These antibodies specifically fix themselves on the Ab–virus–Ab complex (Ac) attached to the support and form a complex marked by the enzyme (Ac–virus–Ac–Ac*), which in turn is revealed by the addition of substrate. In the case of a positive reaction, the destruction of the substrate by the enzyme is generally indicated by a color change.

This technique has been adapted to the analysis of rotaviruses in water (Auberger et al, 1981; Schwartzbrod et al, 1983).

6.4.3.2. Procedure

The technique described below is applied to the search for rotaviruses in the elution liquid that is obtained after water samples have been concentrated.

The reaction is carried out on microplates having 96 wells. First, an anti-rotavirus serum is adsorbed onto the walls of the wells. Then for each elution liquid to be analyzed, a test and a neutralization reaction (or blocking test) are carried out simultaneously, according to the principle illustrated in Figure 6.9, which is applied as follows.

1. The solution to be analyzed is added to wells A and B at 100 μl per hole. If the eluate contains some rotavirus, the particles will attach themselves to the antibodies already adsorbed. After incubation in a humid chamber at 37°C for 90 minutes, one proceeds to a washing with phosphate-buffered saline solution.

2. Antirotavirus immune serum (100 μl) is then added to well B only (blocking test), 100 μl of phosphate-buffered saline solution is added to well A. During incubation for 1 hour at 37°C in a humid chamber, the antibodies that are present in

Test (well A)

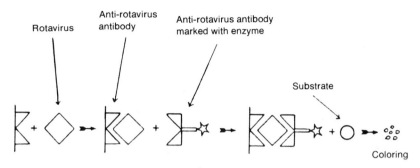

Blocking test (well B)

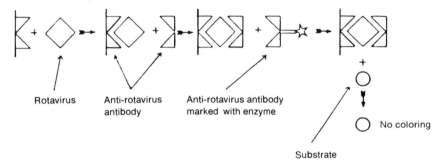

Figure 6.9. Principle of the ELISA test for the detection of rotaviruses.

the serum combine with the rotaviruses that were attached previously. Washing with buffer solution is then performed, to eliminate the noncombined antibodies.

3. To the A (test) and B (blocking test) wells are added the anti-rotavirus immune serum marked with alkaline phosphatase, at 100 μl per well. In case of a positive solution for well A, the marked antibodies will combine with the rotaviruses that were fixed previously. In well B, the marked antibodies will not be able to react because the rotaviruses that were attached to the well have already combined with unmarked antibodies. After incubation in a humid chamber at 37°C for 1 hour, washing in both wells with phosphate-buffered saline solution will eliminate the unattached marked immune serum.

4. The indicator for the two reactions is prepared by the addition to both wells of the substrate of the enzyme, that is, *para*-nitrophenyl phosphate (PNPP), in a ratio of 100 μl of a PNPP solution at 1 mg/ml in diethanolamine buffer at pH 9.8. In the presence of the enzyme (carried by the marked antibodies), the colorless PNPP will be transformed into *para*-nitrophenol, which is yellow. Incubation is carried out in a humid chamber for 1 hour at 37°C, and the reaction is stopped by addition of 25 μl of sodium hydroxide to each well.

If rotavirus is present in the eluate, there is a yellow coloring in the test well (A) and none in the blocking well (B).

In the absence of rotavirus, there is no coloration in either well.

Color is measured with a spectrophotometer (405 nm).

6.4.3.3. Limitations of the Method

The ELISA detection technique has the advantage of being rapid but it has its limits, not only because of its low sensitivity, but also as a result of factors inherent in immunoenzymatic techniques. Indeed, the immunoenzymatic reaction only reveals the presence of rotavirus antigens; it doesn't tell whether these antigens correspond to whole viral particles capable of provoking an infectious syndrome, to degraded, noninfectious viruses, or even to isolated antigenic fractions.

Further research might aid this method for detection in two ways. The first would involve the volume of water to be analyzed and the technique of virus concentration. The other would focus on the validity of the reaction by coupling it with a previous culturing of the rotavirus and success of the ELISA test on the supernatants or homogenates of the culture.

REFERENCES

Auberger, M., Laveran, H., Laluque, J. B., and Beytout, D. (1981) Concentration de rotavirus par adsorption-élution sur poudre de verre. Résultats préliminaires. *J. Fr. Hydrol.* **12**, 229–238.

Bradburne, A. F., Almeida, J. D., Gardner, P. K, Moosat, R. B., Nash, A. A., and Coombs, R. R. A. (1979) A solid-phase system (SPACE) for the detection and quantification off rotavirus in faeces. *J. Gen. Virol.* **44**, 615–623.

Bridger, J. C., and Woode, G. N. (1976) Characterization of two particle types of calf rotaviruses. *J. Gen. Virol.* **31**, 254–260.

Cateigne, G., and Maurin, J. (1965) "Isolement et Etude des Virus dans l'Oeuf Embryonne et en Cultures Cellulaires." La Tourelle, St. Mandé.

Couillin, P., Crainic, R., Cabau, N., Horodniceaunu, F., and Bove, A. (1982) Strain-specific type 1 poliovirus-neutralizing monoclonal antibodies. *Ann. Virol.* **133**(3), 315–323.

Crance, J. M., Deloine, R., Lehevallier, C., Crevat, D., Laveran, H., and Fontanges, R. (1983) Liberation du virus de l'hépatite A dans le milieu de culture lors de sa replication dans les cellules PL/PRF/5. *C.R. Acad. Sci. (Paris)*, **297**, 111–114.

Deetz, T. R., Smith, E. M., Goyal S. M., Gerba, C. P., Vollet, J. J., Tsai, L., Dupont H. L., and Keswik, B. H. Occurrence of rota- and enteroviruses in drinking and environmental water in a developing nation. *Water Res.* **18**, 567–571.

Duermeyer, W. (1980) Application of ELISA for the diagnosis and epidemiology of hepatitis. Doctoral thesis, Utrecht.

Gerba, C. P., Keswik, B. H., Dupont, H. L., and Fields, H. A. (1984) Isolation of rotavirus and hepatitis A virus from drinking water. *Monogr. Virol.* **15**, 119–125.

Jaulmes, C., Jude, A., and Querangal des Essarts, J. (1958) "Pratique du Laboratoire." Masson, Paris.

Kaplikian, A. Z., Wyatt, R. L., Dolin, R., Thornhill, T. S., Kalica, A. R., and Chanok, R. M. (1972) Visualization by immunoelectron microscopy of a 27 nm particle associated with acute infectious nonbacterial gastroenteritis. *J. Virol.* **10**, 1075–1081.

Krembel, C., Dewilde, A., and Herbaut, J. C. (1981) Technique ELISA indirecte pour la detection du rotavirus humain dans les celles. *Pathol. Biol.* **29**, 216–228.

Lwoff, A., and Lwoff, M. (1959) Remarques sur quelques caracteres du developpement du virus de la poliomyélite. *C.R. Acad. Sci.* **248**, 1725–1726.

MacBride, W. D. (1959) Antigenic analysis of poliovirus by kinetic studies of serum neutralization. *Virology*, **7**, 45–48.

Nottay, B. K., Kew, O. M., Hatch, M. H., Heyward, J. T., and Obijeski, F. (1980) Molecular variation of type 1 vaccine related and wild polioviruses during replication in humans. *Virology*, **108**, 405–423.

Schwartzbrod, L., Bennani, A., De Lavergne, E., and Schwartzbrod, J. (1983) Detection des rotavirus dans les eaux usées par immunoenzymologie. Etude préliminaire. *Rev. Fr. Sci. Eau*, **2**, 145–152.

Smith, E. M., and Gerba, C. P. (1982) Development of a method for detection of human rotavirus in water and sewage. *Appl. Environ. Microbiol.* **43**, 1440–1450.

Van Wezel, A. L., and Hazendonk, A. G. (1979) Intratypic serodifferentiation of poliomyelitis virus strains by strain specific-antisera. *Intervirology*, **11**, 2–8.

Chapter 7

METHODS FOR QUANTIFYING RESULTS

Sometimes the quantification of viral particles in a water sample turns out to offer a storehouse of information, allowing one to study the efficiency of a purification system, the variation in the level of viral contamination of a hydrographic network, or the viral dose that will infect a potable water supply. Methods for estimating the number of viruses in a sampling of water are provided in this chapter. However, the results obtained have only a relative and partial value, given the multiple sources of error that are possible during sampling and during numeration in the laboratory. One must keep in mind that a number that is calculated for the viruses in a sampling is at best only proportional to the number of viruses really present in the samples. The proportionality factors (often unknown) depend both on the type of virus present and on the calculation method that is used (Dougherty, 1964).

Because the direct visualization of viruses is usually too complicated and costly, the titration of viral particles uses for the most part indirect methods, which rely on the property of viruses to provoke a specific biological action, which in turn is used in quantification. The process of quantifying viral particles is carried out in three steps:

1. Dilution of the sample.
2. Inoculation into a cell culture of several aliquots of the pure sample and of its dilutions, according to the method selected (eg, under agar medium or in liquid medium).
3. Reading and expression of the results in terms of a mathematical model. There are two types of quantifying the effect of a population of viral particles on cell cultures:
   a. Enumerative types, which consist of counting the number of specific lesions provoked by the viruses
   b. Quantal or "all or nothing" types, which measure the ratio of the number of positive responses (presence of specific lesions) to the total number of possible responses

Only steps 1 and 3 are considered in this chapter; the question of the inoculation onto cell cultures was covered in Chapter 5. One must recall here that for years both virologists and bacteriologists used one or the other method of calculating the results according to which technique of the two was used for cell culture inoculation. Thus, the enumerative type is applied to the plaque technique, and the quantal type is associated with the method of inoculation in liquid medium. We will keep this format, while emphasizing that the results obtained for either counting type are independent of the inoculation technique (Beytout et al, 1975; Maul et al, 1982; Fontuieille and Maul, 1985).

Whichever technique is chosen, the validity of the calculation rests on two essential hypotheses.

1. The presence of one virus is sufficient to provoke a destruction of the cell layer, and the absence of the destruction signifies the absence of virus.
2. The viruses are distributed randomly in the sample; that is, each virus has the same probability of being found in one given inoculum. This hypothesis is valid under two conditions:
   a. The volume of aliquots analyzed be small in relation to the volume of the original sample.
   b. The density of viral particles in the original sample be 50 or greater (Meynell and Meynell, 1970).

7.1. DILUTION OF THE SAMPLES

In every case and without prejudging the viral concentration of the sample, a dilution should be carried out to reduce the number of viral particles to a measurable level and to isolate them. The different operations for dilution are summed up in Figure 7.1.

The dilution factor or ratio is an important parameter for calculating the precision of the results that will be obtained after titration. The factor of one tenth is frequently used because other possible factors, (eg, a half) improve the result but increase the number of flasks or tubes to be inoculated by around threefold. Thus in each case a compromise should be found between the precision wished for and the possible material investment. Furthermore, the dilution liquid should not be chosen haphazardly; or at the very least, once adopted, it should not be changed. Indeed, comparison of several dilution liquids shows very significant differences in the titer of a viral suspension. This is due to the existence of aggregates of viruses (Laveran and Beytout, 1975).

7.2. ENUMERATIVE METHODS

The most usual example of a titration method to which an enumerative type of estimation is applied is the plaque method (cf Chapter 5). The plaque method consists of inoculating cell layers or suspensions and maintaining them in life in an agar medium, which limits the transport of the newly formed viruses to directly adjacent cells. Then the cell layer is stained and the plaques of cellular lysis that form are counted.

Even admitting a proportionality relation between the number of plaques that appear and the initial number of viruses, each lysis plaque is counted as a "plaque-forming unit" (PFU) not as a viral particle. Indeed, one cannot really speak of the number of viruses in the sample because the probability of viral multiplication is unknown in a mixture of virions, and it is impossible to predict the number of virus clumps that will provoke a single lysis plaque.

The calculation of the number of plaque-forming units of a sample varies as a function of the number of plaques counted at one level or at several levels of dilution.

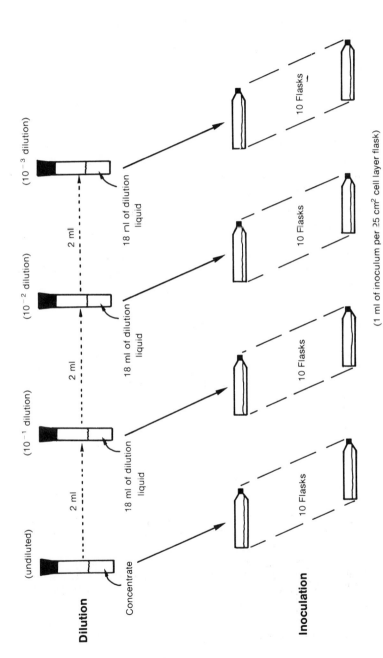

Figure 7.1. Example of the preparation of a decimal dilution for the seeding of a series of cell layers.

Table 7.1. Results for a titration by the plaque method:
Four flasks per dilution; 1 ml of inoculum per flask

Dilution	Number of flasks seeded	Number of plaques counted/flask	Total plaques
1/5	4	30 28 28 24	110/4 ml
1/10	4	13 12 14 17	56/4 ml
1/50	4	2 3 1 3	9/4 ml
1/100	4	0 0 0 0	0/4 ml

Four situations can thus be described, corresponding to the following cases:

1. Fewer than 15 PFU are counted at a level of dilution.
2. From 15 to 100 PFU are counted at one level of dilution.
3. More than 100 PFU are counted at a level of dilution.
4. The results of several successive dilutions are used.

In the example presented in Table 7.1, the number of plaques counted at each level of dilution have been summed. From these data the four possibilities of calculation previously cited are possible.

7.2.1. Fewer Than 15 Plaques at One Level of Dilution

In the example in Table 7.1 the number of plaques obtained at a dilution of 1/50 was smaller than 15. The lower (Ll) and upper (Lu) 95% limits of confidence are calculated from the number ($x = 9$) of plaques and are defined by equations 7.1 and 7.2 (Commissariat a l'Energie Atomique, 1978). They can also be directly read from Table 7.2.

$$Ll = 0.5\chi^2_{0.025}(2x) \tag{7.1}$$

$$Lu = 0.5\chi^2_{0.975}(2x + 2) \tag{7.2}$$

where $\chi^2_{0.025}(2x)$ stands for the chi-square variable with $2x$ degrees of freedom at threshold 0.025, and $\chi^2_{0.975}(2x + 2)$ stands for the chi-square variable with $2x + 2$ degrees of freedom at threshold 0.975.

Under these conditions Ll is 4.11 and Lu is 17.1. Taking into account the dilution factor (1/50) and the number of milliliters inoculated (4 ml), the results should be multiplied by 12.5 to give the density d of the inoculum per milliliter. Thus for $d = 9 \times 12.5$, we have:

$$d = 112.5 \text{ PFU/ml}, \quad \text{with} \quad Ll = 51.4 \text{ and } Lu = 213.8$$

In other words, there is a probability of 95% that the viral density of the inoculum is between 51.4 and 213.8 PFU/ml; the best estimate is 112.5 PFU/ml.

7.2.2. Number of Plaques Counted Between 15 and 100 at One Level of Dilution

In the example in Table 7.1 the number of plaques (x) is 56 at the dilution of 1/10, which falls into the 15100 plaque category. The lower and upper 95% limits of confidence are calculated from the number of plaques and defined by relations 7.3 and 7.4. They can also be read directly from Table 7.2.

$$Ll = 0.25\left[(4x - 1)^{0.5} - 1.96\right]^2 \tag{7.3}$$

$$Lu = 0.25\left[(4x + 3)^{0.5} + 1.96\right]^2 \tag{7.4}$$

In our example Ll is 42 and Lu is 72. Taking into account the dilution factor (1/10) and the number of milliliters inoculated (4 ml), the results should be multiplied by 2.5 to find the density of pure inoculum per milliliter. Under these conditions $d = 56 \times 2.5$, and we write:

$$d = 140 \text{ PFU/ml} \quad \text{with} \quad Ll = 105 \text{ and } Lu = 180$$

In other words, there is a 95% probability that the density of the inoculum is between 105 and 180 PFU/ml; the best estimate is 140 PFU/ml.

7.2.3. MORE THAN 100 PLAQUES AT ONE LEVEL OF DILUTION

In the example in Table 7.1, more than 100 plaques are obtained at a dilution of 1/5. The inferior and superior 95% limits of confidence are calculated from the number ($x = 110$) of plaques and are defined by relations 7.5 and 7.6. They can also be read directly from Table 7.2. These equations represent a simplification of the preceding equations.

$$Ll = -1.96(x)^{0.5} \tag{7.5}$$

$$Lu = +1.96(x)^{0.5} \tag{7.6}$$

In this case Ll is 89.5 and Lu is 130.5. To obtain the viral density per milliliter of pure inoculum and its own confidence limits, it is necessary to take into account the dilution factor and the number of milliliters inoculated at the level of dilution considered. In this example, we multiply the results by 5 (dilution at 1/5) and divide by 4 (4 ml inoculated); and this gives:

$$d = 137.5 \text{ PFU/ml} \quad \text{with} \quad Ll = 111.8 \text{ and } Lu = 163.1$$

In other words, there is a 95% probability that the viral density of the inoculum is between 111.8 and 163.1 PFU/ml, and its best estimation is 137.5 PFU/ml.

7.2.4. Estimation of the Viral Density from Results Taken at Several Levels of Dilution

The estimation of the viral density can be obtained, for example, from the total number of plaques for the first three levels of dilution in Table 7.1.

Table 7.2. Lower (*Ll*) and upper (*Lu*) limits of the 95% confidence level for the densities of plaques (*x*) between 3 and 200

x	Ll	Lu	x	Ll	Lu	x	Ll	Lu	x	Ll	Lu
3	0.6	8.7	51	37.8	66.8	100	81.1	121.4	150	126.7	175.8
4	1.1	10.2	52	38.6	67.9	101	82.0	122.5	151	127.7	176.9
5	1.6	11.6	53	39.5	69.1	102	83.0	123.6	152	128.6	178.0
6	2.2	13.0	54	40.3	70.2	103	83.8	124.7	153	129.5	179.0
7	2.8	14.4	55	41.2	71.3	104	84.8	125.8	154	130.4	180.1
8	3.5	15.7	56	42.1	72.5	105	85.7	126.9	155	131.0	181.2
9	4.1	17.1	57	43.0	73.6	106	86.6	128.0	156	132.3	182.3
10	4.8	18.4	58	43.8	74.7	107	87.5	129.1	157	133.2	183.3
11	5.5	19.7	59	44.7	75.9	108	88.4	130.2	158	134.1	184.4
12	6.2	21.0	60	45.6	77.0	109	89.3	131.2	159	135.0	185.5
13	7.0	22.2	61	46.5	78.1	110	90.2	132.3	160	135.9	186.6
14	7.6	23.5	62	47.3	79.2	111	91.1	133.4	161	136.9	187.4
15	8.2	24.5	63	48.2	80.4	112	92.0	134.5	162	137.8	188.7
16	8.9	25.7	64	49.1	81.5	113	92.9	135.6	163	138.7	189.8
17	9.7	27.0	65	60.1	82.6	114	93.8	136.7	164	139.6	190.9
18	10.5	28.2	66	50.8	83.7	115	94.7	137.8	165	140.6	191.9
19	11.2	29.4	67	51.7	84.8	116	95.6	138.9	166	141.5	193.0
20	12.0	30.6	68	52.6	86.0	117	96.5	140.0	167	142.0	194.1
21	12.8	31.9	69	53.5	87.1	118	97.5	141.1	168	143.3	195.2
22	13.6	33.1	70	54.3	88.2	119	98.4	142.2	169	144.3	196.3
23	14.4	34.3	71	55.2	89.3	120	99.3	143.2	170	145.2	197.3
24	15.2	35.5	72	56.1	90.4	121	100.2	144.0	171	146.1	198.4
25	16.0	36.7	73	57.0	91.6	122	101.1	145.4	172	147.0	199.5
26	16.8	37.8	74	57.9	92.7	123	102.0	146.6	173	148.0	200.5
27	17.6	39.0	75	58.8	93.8	124	102.9	147.6	174	148.9	201.6
28	18.4	40.2	76	59.7	94.9	125	103.8	148.7	175	149.8	202.7
29	19.2	41.4	77	60.5	96.0	126	104.7	149.8	176	150.7	203.7
30	20.0	42.6	78	61.4	97.1	127	105.6	150.9	177	151.7	204.8
31	20.8	43.8	79	62.3	98.2	128	106.6	152.0	178	152.6	206.0
32	21.7	44.9	80	63.2	99.3	129	107.5	153.0	179	153.5	207.0
33	22.5	46.1	81	64.1	100.5	130	108.4	154.1	180	154.4	208.0
34	23.4	47.3	82	65.0	101.6	131	109.3	155.2	181	155.4	209.2
35	24.2	48.4	83	65.9	102.6	132	110.2	156.3	182	156.3	210.2
36	25.0	49.6	84	66.8	103.8	133	111.1	157.4	183	157.2	211.3
37	25.8	50.8	85	67.7	104.9	134	112.0	158.5	184	158.1	212.4
38	26.7	51.9	86	68.6	106.0	135	112.9	159.6	185	159.1	213.4
39	27.5	53.1	87	69.5	107.1	136	113.9	160.7	186	160.0	214.5
40	28.4	54.2	88	70.4	108.2	137	114.8	161.7	187	160.9	215.6
41	29.2	55.4	89	71.3	109.3	138	115.7	162.8	188	161.9	216.6
42	30.0	56.5	90	72.1	110.4	139	116.6	163.9	189	162.8	217.7
43	31.0	57.7	91	73.0	111.5	140	117.5	165.0	190	163.7	218.8
44	31.8	58.8	92	73.9	112.6	141	118.5	166.0	191	164.6	219.9
45	32.6	60.0	93	74.8	113.7	142	119.4	167.2	192	165.6	221.0
46	33.5	61.1	94	75.7	114.8	143	120.3	168.2	193	166.5	222.0
47	34.3	62.3	95	76.6	115.9	144	121.2	169.3	194	167.4	223.1
48	35.2	63.4	96	77.6	117.0	145	122.1	170.4	195	168.4	224.2
49	36.0	64.5	97	78.5	118.1	146	123.1	171.5	196	169.3	225.2
50	36.9	65.7	98	79.3	119.2	147	124.0	172.6	197	170.2	226.3
			99	80.2	120.3	148	124.9	173.6	198	171.2	227.4
						149	125.8	174.7	199	172.1	228.4
									200	173.1	229.5

The inoculum density is estimated by the relation x/A, where x represents the total sum of plaques counted and A is a coefficient that depends on the ratio of dilution and on the number of cell cultures inoculated (Maul et al, 1982). However, this method is satisfactory only when the dilution ratio is small.

In the example in Table 7.1, the number of plaques counted in the three first dilutions is: $x = 110 + 56 + 9 = 175$. The number of viruses in the inoculum of the $1/5$ dilution is estimated by the quotient of x/A (eg, $175/1.6 = 109.4$). This lies between the 95% confidence limits defined by relations 7.7 and 7.8 which resemble relations 7.5 and 7.6, to within the term 1.92.

$$Ll = \frac{\Sigma x}{A} + \frac{1.92 - 1.96\sqrt{\Sigma x}}{A} \qquad (7.7)$$

$$Lu = \frac{\Sigma x}{A} + \frac{1.92 + 1.96\sqrt{\Sigma x}}{A} \qquad (7.8)$$

The symbol A represents the sum of the volumes of samples inoculated per flask at the different levels considered to have generated 175 plaques; that is: $A = 1.6$

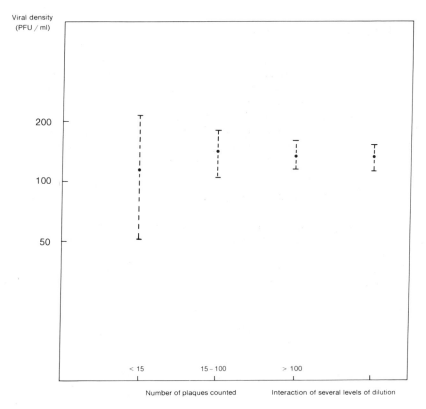

Figure 7.2. Values of the titrations and 95% confidence limits calculated from the results in Table 7.1 as a function of the number of plaques chosen: (a) number of plaques < 15, (b) number of plaques 15–100, (c) number of plaques > 100, (d) plaques counted at several levels of dilution.

= 1 + 1/2 (because we go from a 1/5 dilution to 1/10) + 1/10 (because we continue from a 1/10 dilution to 1/50).

In this example Ll is 94.4 and Lu is 126.8. Taking into account the number of milliliters inoculated at the lowest dilution level (4 ml) and this level of dilution (1/5), the density of the inoculum is $d = 136.8$ PFU/ml, with $Ll = 118$ PFU/ml and $Lu = 158.5$ PFU/ml. In other words, there is a 95% probability that the viral density of the inoculum lies between 118 and 158.5 PFU/ml; the best estimate is 136.8 PFU/ml.

7.2.5. Comparison of the Results

Four results have been obtained from the titration example in Table 7.1. They are given in Figure 7.2.

From the evidence, the amplitude of the confidence intervals increases as the number of counted plaques decreases. The best result is obtained with a large number of plaques. However, the risks of confluence of the lysis plaques are then greatly magnified and the truncation method devised by Beytout et al (1975) should be chosen for calculating the viral titer of the sample.

7.3. QUANTAL NUMERATION METHODS

Three groups of methods can be used for the quantal type of numeration: the estimation of a 50% cytopathic dose (CPD_{50}), the estimation of the most probable number of cytopathic units (MPNCU), and the method of Fisher. Only the first two are presented here. The Fisher method is rather anachronistic, for it makes use of calculations for which part of the information that is furnished by the titration is lost.

These two groups of methods applied to the same titration do not give exactly the same result, and to compare them, we rely as much as possible on an example of titration in liquid medium that is presented in Table 7.3.

7.3.1. The 50% Cytopathic dose (CPD_{50})

The 50% cytopathic dose represents the viral particle concentration of an inoculum that provokes the destruction of a cell layer in half of the cases or with a probability of 0.5 (Figure 7.3).

This value of 50% normally corresponds to the part of the curve for which the slope is the steepest, which gives more precision to the estimation. However, the graphic

Table 7.3. Results for a titration in liquid medium:
10 flasks per dilution; 1 ml of sample per flask

Dilution	Number of flasks seeded	Number of flasks showing a destroyed cell layer
10^{-5}	10	10
10^{-6}	10	9
10^{-7}	10	4
10^{-8}	10	1

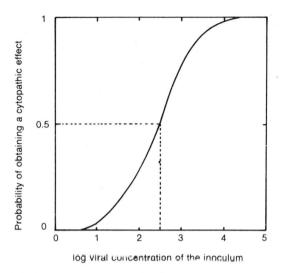

Figure 7.3. Characteristic dose-response curve expressing the relation between the probability of obtaining cell destruction and the logarithm of the inoculum concentration.

determination of the 50% dose from a curve that is experimentally obtained by replacing the probabilities by the observed frequencies is not easy, especially if only some results are available. This is why numerous methods of exploitation have been proposed, including those of Behrens and Kaerber and Reed and Muench (Dougherty, 1964; Van der Waerden, 1967). These methods, which were initially used in toxicology, are not beyond criticism when applied to a titration of viruses on cells (Beytout, 1985); they are, however, frequently used.

7.3.1.1. Calculation of CPD_{50} by the Method of Behrens and Kaerber

This so-called surface method for the calculation of CPD_{50}, described by Behrens and Kaerber, has three interesting qualities. It is, first of all, simple; moreover, it allows for the calculation of a standard deviation, and it does not have a largely restrictive hypothesis serving to support the mathematical development (in particular, it does not suppose the normality of the distribution and necessitates only rather simple hypotheses, viz, a symmetric distribution and percentages of response between 0 and 100%).

According to Behrens and Kaerber, the logarithm of the viral dose provoking cell layer destruction in 50% of the inoculated flasks is given by the following formula:

$$\log CPD_{50} = l_r + \tfrac{1}{2}d - d \sum_{i=0}^{r} h_i \qquad (7.9)$$

where l_r = logarithm of the highest dilution that still gives a 100% positive response, and is given index r
  d = logarithm of the dilution ratio
  h_i = proportion of positive response at a level of dilution i

Table 7.4. Calculation of the proportions of positive responses
from the results of a titration in liquid medium

Dilution	Number of positive responses[a]	Proportion of responses Positive responses, h	Complements, $1 - h$
10^{-5}	10/10	1	0
10^{-6}	9/10	0.9	0.1
10^{-7}	4/10	0.4	0.6
10^{-8}	1/10	0.1	0.9

[a] Positive: cytopathic effect confirmed by subculture.

The standard deviation is equal to:

$$\sigma = d\sqrt{\sum_{i=0}^{r} \frac{h_i(1 - h_i)}{n_i - 1}} \tag{7.10}$$

where n_i is the number of trials carried out at dilution i.

Using the example in Table 7.3, where the dilution ratio is one-tenth, it is possible to calculate the proportion of positive responses (h) and its complement ($1 - h$). These are given in Table 7.4.

From these results one can calculate that:

$$\log CPD_{50} = -5 + 1/2(1) - (2.4) = -6.90$$

and

$$\sigma = \sqrt{\frac{(0.9)(0.1)}{9} + \frac{(0.4)(0.6)}{9} + \frac{(0.1)(0.9)}{9}} = 0.22$$

from which $CPD_{50} = 10^{-6.90 \pm 0.22}$.

The 95% confidence limits are obtained by equations 7.11 and 7.12:

$$\log Ll = \log CPD - 1.96/\sigma \tag{7.11}$$

$$\log Lu = \log CPD + 1.96/\sigma \tag{7.12}$$

if the logarithm of the CPD_{50} is considered to be normally distributed.

7.3.1.2. *Calculation of CPD$_{50}$ by the Method of Reed and Muench*

In the method of Reed and Muench the CPD_{50} is obtained by linear interpolation from the cumulated frequencies of the positive and negative responses. The calculation is founded on the principle according to which any host infected by a virus at a given concentration might have also been attacked at a higher concentration, and vice versa. Using the example in Table 7.3, it is possible to calculate the cumulative totals of positive and negative responses (Table 7.5).

Table 7.5. Calculation of the cumulative totals of positive and negative responses obtained from a titration in liquid medium

Dilution	Number of positive responses[a]	Number of negative responses	Cumulated positive responses	Cumulated negative responses	Cumulative frequency of the positive responses
10^{-5}	10	0	24	0	100%
10^{-6}	9	1	14	1	93.3%
10^{-7}	4	6	5	7	41.7%
10^{-8}	1	9	1	16	5.9%

[a] Positive: cytopathic effect confirmed by subculture.

The CPD_{50} is calculated from the following relation:

$$\log CPD_{50} = \log d_l - \frac{f_l - 50}{f_l - f_u}$$

where d_l = dilution < CPD_{50}
f_l = % of frequency < CPD_{50}
f_u = % of frequency > CPD_{50}

From the example calculated in Table 7.5, the CPD_{50} lies between 10^{-6} and 10^{-7}, which corresponds to cumulative frequencies of 93.3 and 41.7%, respectively. By linear interpolation, we obtain:

$$\log CPD_{50} = -6 - \frac{(93.3 - 50)}{(93.3 - 41.7)} = -6.84$$

$$CPD_{50} = 10^{-6.84}$$

This method should not be employed on a priority basis because its precision is difficult to evaluate. Furthermore, a result that is calculated on the basis of cumulative frequencies leads one to believe that the estimation has been done from more numbers of positive responses than were in fact involved.

7.3.2. The Most Probable Number of Cytopathic Units (MPNCU)

Like the preceding approaches, the method for the estimation of the most probable number of cytopathic units uses the results furnished by the inoculation of cell layers by a viral suspension that has or has not been diluted and has been subdivided into several fractions. This method relies on the principle of the maximum of likelihood. The most probable number of cytopathic units is calculated from a collection of positive results obtained for three successive dilutions. The term "positive result" means destruction of a cell layer that is confirmed by subculture.

The MPNCU is estimated by the value corresponding to the maximum of the likelihood function $L(u)$ which, at each value of the viral density u, associates the probability of the appearance of the triplet of results used (triplet or characteristic triplet).

The equation to be solved is complex, and its resolution calls for the use of calculators or tables. Finally, the MPN is the solution of equation 7.13 for the unknown λ corresponding to the maximum of the likelihood function (Wyshak and Detre, 1972).

$$\sum_{i=1}^{k} (n_i - p_i)v_i = \sum_{i=1}^{k} \frac{p_i v_i e^{-\lambda v_i}}{1 - e^{-\lambda v_i}} \tag{7.13}$$

where k represents the number of dilutions, p_i the number of positive responses obtained for the dilution of rank i, and v_i designates the volume of the inoculum seeded in each one of the n_i media of the dilution of order i.

The lower (Ll) and upper (Lu) limits of a confidence interval at threshold $(1 - \alpha)$, with $\alpha = \alpha_1 + \alpha_2$, are given by relations 7.14 and 7.15.

$$Ll = \frac{1}{2k}\chi^2_{\alpha/2}(\nu_1), \quad \text{with} \quad \nu_1 = 2\Sigma r_i = 2k\bar{r} \tag{7.14}$$

$$Lu = \frac{1}{2k}\chi^2_{1-\alpha/2}(\nu_2), \quad \text{with} \quad \nu_2 = 2(\Sigma r_i + 1) = 2(k\bar{r} + 1) \tag{7.15}$$

where the quantity $\chi^2_p(\nu)$ represents the Pearson variable with the threshold of probability p with ν degrees of freedom, which may be read directly from a table of chi-square values (Fontuieille and Maul, 1985).

Figure 7.4 represents graphically the logarithm of this likelihood function for an arbitrarily chosen triplet. The most probable number is defined by the modal value of this function.

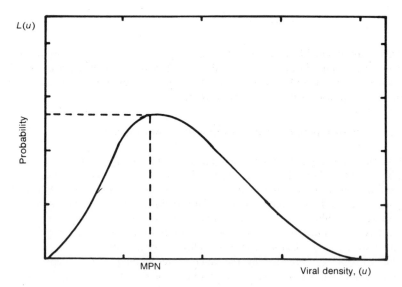

Figure 7.4. Graph of the likelihood function $L(u)$ (probability of the triplet versus viral density).

Table 7.6. Importance of the bias and value of the precision of the MPN as a function of the number of flasks or tubes seeded at each dilution level: Factor of dilution = 10

Number of seeded flasks	Importance of the bias (%)	Precision of the result (%)[a]
3	31	80
5	18	60
10	8	40
96	1	13

[a] The precision can fluctuate above or below the indicated values as a function of the viral density of the inoculum.
Source: After Maul (1980).

The frequency curve of the MPN is a bell-shaped curve that is biased to the right. This asymmetry has two consequences:

1. The results are biased; that is, the MPN overestimates the real viral density ν
2. For a small number of inocula per dilution, the properties of the normal distribution cannot be used to calculate the 95% confidence intervals.

These inconveniences can be corrected by using not the MPN itself but its logarithm and by increasing the number of flasks inoculated per dilution. Under these conditions one can make the following observations:

The asymmetry of the curve is reduced.

The distribution is very close to the normal law and allows a calculation of the limits of confidence.

The relative bias diminishes in a spectacular manner, and the precision of the result is considerably increased.

Indeed, as is shown in Table 7.6, the use of three to five inocula per level of dilution cannot be accepted, considering the overestimation of the results by around 30% and a precision as bad as 80%. On the other hand, the use of 96 inocula per dilution perfectly resolves this problem (Hugues, 1981; Prost and Hugues, 1982).

Thus, a compromise should be sought between the expected precision of the result and the number of flasks or tubes to be inoculated. If the laboratory can support the cost, the number of inocula for each level of dilution should be quite large.

We will consider four examples: calculation of the MPN for results obtained after a dilution of 10 and following in steps of 10 with 5, 10, and 96 inocula per dilution, and calculation of the MPN for results obtained at one level of dilution (or without dilution).

When they exist, tables relating the triplets of results (characteristic numbers) to the MPN and to their limits of confidence will be presented.

The 95% limits of confidence have been calculated with relations 7.16 and 7.17, which represent a first approximation not taking into account certain fluctuations connected to the viral density of the inocula.

$$Ll = \frac{\text{MPN}}{C} \tag{7.16}$$

$$Lu = \text{MPN} C \cdot C \tag{7.17}$$

Table 7.7. Values of C as a function of the dilution ratio and of the number of inocula per dilution

Number of inocula per dilution	Dilution Ratio			
	2	4	5	10
3	2.23	3.10	3.39	4.68
5	1.86	2.41	2.58	3.30
10	1.55	1.86	1.95	2.32
96	1.15	1.22	1.24	1.29

Source: Adapted from Cochran (1950).

where C represents a particular value, which is a function of the number of inocula per dilution and of the ratio of dilution. Table 7.7 gives the values of C for 3, 5, 10, and 96 inocula per dilution and for the dilution ratios of 2, 4, 5, and 10.

7.3.2.1. Case of 5 Inocula per Dilution

As an example, let us take the titrations whose results are given in Table 7.8.

The characteristic triplet 5, 4, 1 corresponds to the dilution triplet of 10^{-5}, 10^{-6}, and 10^{-7}. Table 7.9 gives an MPN of 17, corresponding to the volume of inoculum for a flask with the smallest dilution of the triplet of results used. The 95% confidence limits presented in the third column of the same table are 7 and 48, respectively. Taking into account the dilution factor, one can say that there is a probability of 95% that the viral density of the inoculum is between 7×10^5 and 48×10^5 MPNCU/ml. The best estimate is 17×10^5 MPNCU/ml. The amplitude of these confidence intervals considerably limits the usefulness of the results for certain mathematical studies.

7.3.2.2. Case of 10 Inocula per Dilution

The following reasoning comes from the titration results that are presented in Table 7.3. From this table two triplets of results can be used for the calculation of viral density, namely 10, 9, 4 and 9, 4, 1. In this case we can use these two triplets, then take the arithmatic mean of the logarithms of the two MPN found. In practice, the triplet

Table 7.8. Results of a titration in liquid medium: 5 flasks per dilution; 1 ml of dilution per flask

Dilution	Number of flasks inoculated	Number of positive flasks[a]
10^{-5}	5	5
10^{-6}	5	4
10^{-7}	5	1
10^{-8}	5	0

[a] Positive: cytopathic effect confirmed by subculture.

Table 7.9. Most probable number of cytopathic units (MPNCU) and 95% confidence intervals calculated from the triplet of results for 5 inocula per dilution: 1 ml per flask, dilution factor = 10

Characteristic number			MPNCU	95% Confidence limits	
0	0	0	< 0.2		
0	0	1	0.2	< 0.1	1.0
0	1	0	0.2	< 0.1	1.0
0	1	1	0.4	< 0.1	1.3
0	2	0	0.4	< 0.1	1.3
1	0	0	0.2	< 0.1	1.1
1	0	1	0.4	0.1	1.5
1	1	0	0.4	0.1	1.5
1	1	1	0.6	0.2	1.8
1	2	0	0.6	0.2	1.8
1	2	1	0.8	0.3	2.1
1	3	0	0.8	0.3	2.1
2	0	0	0.4	0.1	1.7
2	0	1	0.7	0.2	2.0
2	1	0	0.7	0.2	2.1
2	1	1	0.9	0.3	2.4
2	2	0	0.9	0.3	2.5
2	2	1	1.2	0.5	2.9
2	3	0	1.2	0.5	2.9
3	0	0	0.8	0.3	2.4
3	0	1	1.1	0.4	2.9
3	0	2	1.3	0.6	3.4
3	1	0	1.1	0.4	2.9
3	1	1	1.4	0.6	3.5
3	1	2	1.7	0.7	3.9
3	2	0	1.4	0.6	3.5
3	2	1	1.7	0.7	4.0
3	3	0	1.7	0.7	4.1
3	3	1	2.1	1.0	4.6
3	4	0	2.1	0.9	4.7
4	0	0	1.3	0.5	3.8
4	0	1	1.7	0.7	4.5
4	0	2	2.1	0.9	5.3
4	1	0	1.7	0.7	4.6
4	1	1	2.1	0.9	5.5
4	1	2	2.6	1.2	6.3
4	2	0	2.2	0.9	5.6
4	2	1	2.6	1.2	6.5
4	2	2	3.2	1.5	7.4
4	3	0	2.7	1.2	6.7
4	3	1	3.3	1.5	7.7
4	3	2	3.9	1.9	8.6
4	4	0	3.4	1.6	8.0
4	4	1	4.0	1.9	9.0
4	5	0	4	0.9	9.0
5	0	0	2.3	0.9	8.6
5	0	1	3.0	1	11
5	0	2	4	2	14
5	1	0	3	1	12
5	1	1	5	2	15

Table 7.9. *Continued*

	Characteristic number		MPNCU	95% Confidence	limits
5	1	2	6	3	18
5	1	3	8	4	22
5	2	0	5	2	17
5	2	1	7	3	21
5	2	2	9	4	25
5	2	3	12	5	29
5	3	0	8	3	25
5	3	1	11	4	30
5	3	2	14	6	36
5	3	3	17	8	41
5	3	4	21	10	48
5	4	0	13	5	39
5	4	1	17	7	48
5	4	2	22	10	58
5	4	3	28	12	69
5	4	4	35	16	82
5	5	0	24	10	94
5	5	1	30	10	130
5	5	2	50	20	200
5	5	3	90	30	290
5	5	4	160	60	530

Source: After De Man (1977).

whose intermediate term is closest to 80% of the positive results is chosen, because its statistical value is the largest.

The tables of Halvorson and Ziegler (Table 7.10) give the value of the MPN per milliliter for the titrations carried out under these conditions. Thus, to the triplet 10, 9, 4 the probability function associates the MPN of 29.8. Taking into account the dilution, the viral density $d = 29.8 \times 10^5$ or $d = 3 \times 10^6$ MPNCU/ml, and the 95% confidence limits are:

$$Ll = \frac{29.8}{2.32} = 12.8 \quad \text{and} \quad Lu = 29.8 \times 2.32 = 69.1$$

The value of the factor C (2.32) is taken from Table 7.7.

It is then possible to say that there is a probability of 95% that the viral density is between 1.28×10^6 and 6.91×10^6 MPNCU/ml, its best estimate is 3×10^6 MPNCU/ml.

7.3.2.3. Case of More Than 40 Inocula per Dilution

A titration carried out with more than 40 inocula per dilution permits one to reduce considerably the bias of the MPN and to obtain an acceptable precision. However, it is not feasible to attempt to manipulate 40 or more flasks per dilution. That is why Hugues (1981) has proposed using 96-well cell culture plates (eg, Microtest II).

Table 7.10. Most probable number of cytopathic units (MPNCU) calculated from the triplet of results for 10 inocula per dilution, 1 ml per flask, and a dilution ratio of 10

Characteristic number			MPNCU	Characteristic number			MPNCU
10	10	9	230	10	3	3	6.62
10	10	8	162	10	3	2	5.61
10	10	7	120	10	3	1	4.74
10	10	6	91.8	10	3	0	3.99
10	10	5	70.2	10	2	4	6.31
10	10	4	54.2	10	2	3	5.34
10	10	3	42.8	10	2	2	4.56
10	10	2	34.9	10	2	1	3.88
10	10	1	27.5	10	2	0	3.29
10	10	0	24.0	10	1	3	4.42
10	9	9	60.7	10	1	2	3.76
10	9	8	52.6	10	1	1	3.17
10	9	7	45.8	10	1	0	2.75
10	9	6	39.8	10	0	2	3.14
10	9	5	34.6	10	0	1	2.68
10	9	4	29.8	10	0	0	2.31
10	9	3	26.3	9	8	0	4.99
10	9	2	22.8	9	7	1	4.88
10	9	1	19.7	9	7	0	4.35
10	9	0	17.0	9	6	2	4.74
10	8	7	31.0	9	6	1	4.25
10	8	6	27.8	9	6	0	3.81
10	8	5	21.9	9	5	2	4.16
10	8	4	22.1	9	5	1	3.72
10	8	3	19.6	9	5	0	3.34
10	8	2	17.1	9	4	3	4.08
10	8	1	15.0	9	4	2	3.65
10	8	0	13.0	9	4	1	3.24
10	7	6	21.9	9	4	0	2.90
10	7	5	19.5	9	3	3	3.62
10	7	4	17.4	9	3	2	3.24
10	7	3	15.3	9	3	1	2.88
10	7	2	13.3	9	3	0	2.55
10	7	1	11.6	9	2	3	3.16
10	7	0	10.1	9	2	2	2.84
10	6	6	17.5	9	2	1	2.53
10	6	5	15.7	9	2	0	2.23
10	6	4	14.1	9	1	2	2.49
10	6	3	12.5	9	1	1	2.21
10	6	2	10.9	9	1	0	1.93
10	6	1	9.33	9	0	2	2.17
10	6	0	7.92	9	0	1	1.91
10	5	5	13.0	9	0	0	1.64
10	5	4	11.5	8	6	0	2.7
10	5	3	10.2	8	5	1	2.67
10	5	2	8.72	8	5	0	2.42
10	5	1	7.42	8	4	2	2.66
10	5	0	6.22	8	4	1	2.4
10	4	5	10.73	8	4	0	2.17
10	4	4	9.43	8	3	2	2.39
10	4	3	8.18	8	3	1	2.14
10	4	2	7.0	8	3	0	1.93
10	4	1	5.89	8	2	3	2.33
10	4	0	4.93	8	2	2	2.1
10	3	4	7.73	8	2	1	1.88

Table 7.10. *Continued*

Characteristic number			MPNCU	Characteristic number			MPNCU
8	2	0	1.69	5	1	1	0.86
8	1	2	1.87	5	1	0	0.73
8	1	1	1.66	5	0	2	0.85
8	1	0	1.47	5	0	1	0.72
8	0	2	1.66	5	0	0	0.6
8	0	1	1.46	4	5	0	1.06
8	0	0	1.28	4	4	0	0.93
7	6	0	2.12	4	3	1	0.92
7	5	1	2.09	4	3	0	0.8
7	5	0	1.91	4	2	1	0.8
7	4	2	2.08	4	2	0	0.68
7	4	1	1.88	4	1	2	0.8
7	4	0	1.71	4	1	1	0.68
7	3	2	1.88	4	1	0	0.56
7	3	1	1.69	4	0	2	0.67
7	3	0	1.52	4	0	1	0.56
7	2	2	1.67	4	0	0	0.45
7	2	1	1.5	3	4	0	0.76
7	2	0	1.33	3	3	2	0.86
7	1	2	1.49	3	3	1	0.75
7	1	1	1.32	3	3	0	0.64
7	1	0	1.16	3	2	1	0.64
7	0	2	1.32	3	2	0	0.53
7	0	1	1.16	3	1	2	0.64
7	0	0	1.01	3	1	1	0.53
6	5	0	1.55	3	1	0	0.43
6	4	2	1.71	3	0	2	0.52
6	4	1	1.55	3	0	1	0.42
6	4	0	1.39	3	0	0	0.32
6	3	2	1.53	2	4	0	0.62
6	3	1	1.38	2	3	0	0.51
6	3	0	1.23	2	2	0	0.41
6	2	2	1.37	2	1	1	0.4
6	2	1	1.22	2	1	0	0.3
6	2	0	1.07	2	0	2	0.4
6	1	2	1.21	2	0	1	0.3
6	1	1	1.06	2	0	0	0.2
6	1	0	0.92	1	3	0	0.38
6	0	2	1.06	1	2	1	0.38
6	0	1	0.92	1	2	0	0.29
6	0	0	0.78	1	1	1	0.28
5	5	0	1.28	1	1	0	0.19
5	4	1	1.27	1	0	1	0.19
5	4	0	1.14	1	0	0	0.11
5	3	1	1.13	0	2	0	0.18
5	3	0	1.00	0	1	1	0.18
5	2	2	1.13	0	1	0	0.09
5	2	1	0.99	0	0	1	0.09
5	2	0	0.86				
5							

Source: After Halvorson and Ziegler in Meynell and Meynell (1970).

Table 7.11. Results of a titration on microplates: 96 wells per dilution, 25 μl of inoculum per well

Dilution	Number of inocula	Number of positive wells[a]
10^{-1}	96	94
10^{-2}	96	49
10^{-3}	96	10

[a] Positive: cytopathic effect confirmed by subculture.

Without excessive costs in materials or time, it is possible to inoculate a plate with its 96 or fewer wells (minimum of 40) for each dilution of the sample (25 μl of inoculum per well). The number of wells presenting a cytopathic effect that is confirmed by subculture is then recorded.

Table 7.11 gives an example of the results of a titration performed with this technique.

The most probable number of cytopathic units corresponding to the triplet 94, 49, 10 is given by the solution of equation 7.18 for unknown (u)

$$(96 - p_1) + 0.1(96 - p_2) + 0.01(96 - p_3) = \frac{p_1 e^{-u}}{1 - e^{-u}} + \frac{0.1 p_2 e^{-0.1u}}{1 - e^{-0.1u}} + \frac{0.01 p_3 e^{-0.01u}}{1 - e^{-0.01u}}$$

$$(7.18)$$

where p_1, p_2, and p_3 are the values of the positive results for the three dilutions considered. This equation, which is a particular case of equation 7.13, is of the form $f(u) - k = 0$ (Fig. 7.5). Its resolution necessitates the use of a calculator. Different programs for the solution of the probability equation by the method of Newton have already been proposed (Hugues and Plantat, 1982), and an example is given in Table 7.12.

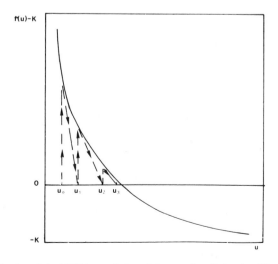

Figure 7.5. Determination of the MPN by resolution of the equation $f(u) - k = 0$ by Newton's method.

Table 7.12. A Hewlett-Packard 41 C calculator program for solving the probability equation in the case of three decimal dilutions[a]

01 LBL "MPN"	36 "INITIAL"	71 +	106 0.0001
02 "N1"	37 PROMPT	72 RCL 02	107 *
03 PROMPT	38 STO 04	73 RCL 07	108 1
04 STO 11	39 LBL 01	74 *	109 RCL 07
05 "P 1"	40 CHS	75 0.01	110 -
06 PROMPT	41 E**X	76 *	111 X**2
07 STO 00	42 STO 05	77 1	112 /
08 "N2"	43 RCL 04	78 RCL 07	113 -
09 PROMPT	44 0.1	79 -	114 STO 09
10 STO 12	45 *	80 /	115 RCL 03
11 "P2"	46 CHS	81 +	116 RCL 08
12 PROMPT	47 E**X	82 STO 08	117 -
13 STO 01	48 STO 06	83 RCL 00	118 RCL 04
14 "N3"	49 RCL 04	84 RCL 05	119 RCL 09
15 PROMPT	50 0.01	85 *	120 *
16 STO 13	51 *	86 1	121 +
17 "P3"	52 CHS	87 RCL 05	122 RCL 09
18 PROMPT	53 E**X	88 -	123 /
19 STO 02	54 STO 07	89 X**2	124 STO 10
20 RCL 11	55 RCL 00	90 /	125 RCL 04
21 RCL 00	56 RCL 05	91 CHS	126 -
22 -	57 *	92 RCL 01	127 ABS
23 RCL 12	58 1	93 RCL 06	128 0.01
24 RCL 01	59 RCL 05	94 *	129 X>Y ?
25 -	60 -	95 0.01	130 GTO 02
26 0.1	61 /	96 *	131 RCL 10
27 *	62 RCL 01	97 1	132 STO 04
28 +	63 RCL 06	98 RCL 06	133 GTO 01
29 RCL 13	64 *	99 -	134 LBL 02
30 RCL 02	65 0.1	100 X**2	135 RCL 10
31 -	66 *	101 /	
32 0.01	67 1	102 -	
33 *	68 RCL 06	103 RCL 02	
34 +	69 -	104 RCL 07	
35 STO 03	70 /	105 *	

[a] The usual "up-arrow" sign has been replaced by **.

From the triplet of results in the preceding example, the most probable number of cytopathic units is 2.46×10^3/ml. The 95% confidence limits can be calculated with the aid of factor C in Table 7.7, that is, 1.29. Under these conditions, there is a 95% probability that the viral density of the inoculum is between 1.90×10^3 and 3.17×10^3 MPNCU/ml; the best estimate is 2.46×10^3 MPNCU/ml.

7.3.2.4. Analysis of the Results Obtained from a Single Dilution

In a certain number of cases it is not possible to use a triplet of results, either because the small viral density of the sample does not permit dilution or because certain levels of dilution have been shown to be unfeasible because of toxicity, bacterial contamination, breakage of flasks, and so on. The method can be recommended and used only with a minimum of 30 inoculated flasks or tubes, which permits acceptable precision. The most probable number of cytopathic units per milliliter of dilution is given by relation 7.19.

$$\text{MPNCU} = \frac{1}{v_i} 2.303 \times \log \frac{n}{X} \tag{7.19}$$

where v_i = volume of the inoculum
n = number of inocula
X = number of negative inocula

The 95% confidence limits are given by relations 7.20 and 7.21 and can be applied only if both the number of positive inoculated tubes and the number of negative inoculated tubes are larger than 5.

$$Ll = -\frac{1}{v_i} 2.303 \log \left\{ \frac{X}{n} + \frac{1.96}{n} \sqrt{\frac{X(n-X)}{n}} \right\} \tag{7.20}$$

$$Lu = -\frac{1}{v_i} 2.303 \log \left\{ \frac{X}{n} - \frac{1.96}{n} \sqrt{\frac{X(n-X)}{n}} \right\} \tag{7.21}$$

An example can be taken from Table 7.11.

Only the 10^{-2} dilution is feasible with 49 wells out of the 96 presenting a characteristic CPE for a theoretical zone of density where the standard deviation of the base 10 logarithm of the distribution of the MPN varies slightly (Fontuieille and Maul, 1985).

Equations 7.19, 7.20, and 7.21 permit one to calculate as follows:

$$\text{viral density} = 2.85 \times 10^3 \text{ MPNCU/ml}$$

$$Ll = 2.11 \times 10^3 \text{ MPNCU/ml}$$

$$Lu = 3.77 \times 10^3 \text{ MPNCU/ml}$$

7.4. CHOICE OF A METHOD OF QUANTIFICATION

The choice of a quantification method can be discussed on two levels because, as pointed out at the beginning of this chapter, the methods of seeding and estimating viral density from cytological results are mutually independent.

The technique of inoculation under nutritive agar medium presents the considerable advantage of individualizing the plaque-forming units. Indeed, despite its limitations (cf Chapter 5), it remains widely used and is an unofficial method of reference.

The technique of inoculation in liquid medium is used by various laboratories for the titration of viral suspensions. It has been disparaged for a long time because it is still badly used (3–5 inocula per dilution) and is still associated with a method of estimation (eg, MPN) that under these conditions gives very bad precision and a large bias. In fact, inoculation in liquid medium presents certain advantages (cf Chapter 5) and allows automation of the subcultures of the titrations carried out on a microplate.

The works of Hugues (1981) have shown good correspondence between the PFU and the most probable number (calculated from 96 inocula per dilution), and some relations have been calculated between CPD_{50} and the PFU, such as:

$$1 \text{ CPD}_{50} = 0.69 \text{ PFU}$$

Table 7.13. Comparison of the titrations and confidence limits obtained by different methods based on the results in Table 7.4

Estimation method of the viral density	Calculated viral density (log/ml)	95% Confidence limits	
		Ll	*Lu*
CPD_{50} (Behrens and Kaerber)	6.90	6.47	7.33
CPD_{50} (Reed and Muench)[a]	6.84	—	—
MPN (triplet)	6.47	6.11	6.84
Fisher[b]	6.66	6.23	7.0

[a] Confidence limits not determined.
[b] For the purpose of comparison.

and

$$1 \text{ PFU} = 1.44 \text{ CPD}_{50}$$

Yet the different methods of calculation do not have the same advantages. Thus, in the enumerative type the precision (and consequently, the confidence interval) is a function of the number of lyses or of the number of observed lysis plaques. If the number is small, the precision is small, and vice versa. Consequently, the analysis of variance cannot be systematically applied in the comparison of the results because it is sometimes difficult to find an adequate transformation to use in homogenizing the variances. On the contrary, the quantal type of method, with the technique for the calculation of the MPN, has the certain advantage of giving a result whose precision depends above all on the number of inocula carried out at each level of dilution. Under these conditions, the analysis of variance for comparing the results can be applied in most cases. In deciding a sufficient number of inocula, the quantal type of estimation meets the essential conditions of the quality, that is:

To give reliable results (small confidence interval)
To be convergent (to give better results when the number of individuals observed or analyzed increases)
To be un-biased or only slightly biased.

Although obtained by methods with different concepts, the results of the titrations calculated in the preceding sections are comparable (Table 7.13).

The three calculation techniques—CPD_{50} (method of Behrens and Kaerber), most probable number from a triplet of results, and the Fisher approach—give very similar results whose 95% confidence limits largely overlap (Table 7.13). However, the CPD_{50} method is appropriate only if the levels of dilution ie, well in the 50% zone), and the Fisher method loses part of the information because levels of dilution are not differentiated. The MPN method is more reliable than the others and thus may be preferentially used on condition that the number of inocula per dilution be greater than 30.

Whichever method of calculation is chosen by the analyst, it is advisable to recall once again that the result is only an estimation of the real density of the viral suspension to be analyzed and that it should be bracketed by its confidence limits.

REFERENCES

Beytout, D. (1985) Le titrage des virus. In "Virologie Medicale," J. Maurin, Ed. Flammarion, Paris, 294–309.

Beytout, D., Laveran, H., and Reynaud, M. P. (1975) Méthode pratique d'évaluation numerique applicable aux techniques miniaturisées de titrage en plages. *Ann. Biol. Clin.* **33**, 379–384.

Commissariat a l'Energie Atomique (1978) "Statistique Appliquée a l'Exploitation des Mesures," Masson, Paris.

Cochran, W. G. (1950) Estimation of bacterial densities by means of the "most probable number." *Biometrics*, **6**, 105–112.

De Man, J. C. (1977) MPN tables for more than one test. *Eur. J. Appl. Microbiol. Biotechnol.* **4**, 307–316.

Dougherty, R. M. (1964) Animal virus titrations. In "Techniques in Experimental Virology," C. Harris, Ed. Academic Press, London, pp. 169–223.

Fontuieille, D., and Maul H. (1985) Dénombrement et mesures d'activité des bactéries. In "Bactériologie des Milieux Aquatiques: Aspects Ecologiques et Sanitaires," G. Martin, Ed. Lavoisier, Paris.

Hugues, B. (1981) Nouvelle utilisation du nombre le plus probable en virologie. Application à la mise en evidence et à la quantification des virus dans le milieu hydrique. Doctoral these, Universite de Metz.

Hugues, B., and Plantat, J. L. (1982) Calcul du nombre le plus probable et de son intervalle de confiance dans le cas ou le nombre d'inoculums par dilution est important. *Chemosphere*, **11**, 1135–1140.

Laveran, H., and Beytout, D. (1975) Influence de quelques substances sur le titre apparent d'un polio-virus en suspension aqueuse. *Ann. Microbiol. (Inst. Pasteur)*, **126A**, 123–126.

Maul, A. (1980) Etude des méthodes de quantification en microbiologie. D.E.A. d'Ecotoxicologie, Universite de Metz.

Maul, A., Dollard, M. A., and Block, J. C. (1981) Application du principe du maximum de vraisemblance (NPP) au titrage bactérien sur milieu gelose. *J. Fr. Hydrol.* **12**, 245–254.

Meynell, G. G., and Meynell, E. (1970) "Theory and Practice in Experimental Bacteriology," 2nd ed. University Press, Cambridge.

Prost, H., and Hugues, B. (1982) Dénombrement des microorganismes par la technique du nombre le plus probable (NPP): Emploi statistique de cet indice. *Ann. Fals. Chim.* **75**, 185–207.

Van der Waerden, B. L. (1967) "Statistique Mathématique." Dunod, Paris.

Wyshak, G., and Detre, K. (1972) Estimating the number of organisms in quantal assays. *Appl. Microbiol.* **23**(4), 784–900.

Chapter 8

ORGANIZATION OF A VIROLOGY LABORATORY FOR WATER SYSTEMS

The requirements of a virology laboratory are understandably different from those of a bacteriology laboratory. There is no single model for such a laboratory, and considerations such as available space and cost are not the least among those that can influence the choice of a structure or equipment. In seeking an optimum, one should follow at least four rules.

1. Provide for independent work units, in order to eliminate contamination.
2. Correctly equip each work unit as much as possible, to ensure the most efficient work space and to minimize movements.
3. Assure the asepsis of the manipulations under all circumstances, thus avoiding the contamination of the samples, chemical reactants, and cell cultures.
4. Assure the protection of all those working in the laboratory, in case of accidents.

8.1. DEFINITIONS OF WORK UNITS

A laboratory carrying out virological analysis of water systems by the inoculation of cell cultures can be organized in five independent work units. The term "work unit" means either a room, or a work area that is well separated from the rest of a large room.

8.1.1. Unit for Waste, Surface, and Recreational Waters

The concentration of a priori contaminated waters is carried out in one unit, as well as the decontamination of different samples (eg, untreated wastewaters, elution liquids).

8.1.2. Work Unit for Potable Water

The unit for potable water samples should be reserved solely for waters that are a priori noncontaminated. In this zone concentration and decontamination operations are carried out.

8.1.3. Unit for Cell Cultures

An area is kept for cell culture and for preparation of the different media and solutions necessary for cell culture. Only the changing of media, trypsinations, and

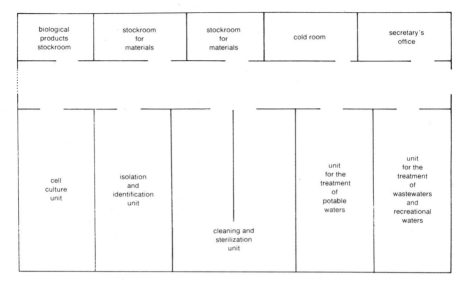

Figure 8.1. Proposed layout for a water virology laboratory.

sterilizing filtrations are carried out here. Samples containing bacteria or viruses should never be handled in this unit.

8.1.4. Isolation and Identification Unit

Another unit is reserved for the inoculation of cell cultures and microscopic observation of the cytopathic effects, for subcultures, and for the identification of isolated viruses. Only decontaminated samples should ever be present in this unit.

8.1.5. Cleaning and Sterilization Unit

The final unit should be divided into two parts: one kept for the sterilization of the contaminated material and for washing, the other destined for the preparation and sterilization of clean material. It is advisable to join to this unit a cold room that is large enough to stock the different products and the media that are currently used in virology. Note that if the laboratory works with animals (eg, newborn mice), a totally separate animal room should be provided.

Figure 8.1 is a diagram of a virology laboratory. This floor plan is designed to limit the comings and goings between different units and is organized around the cleaning and sterilization area.

8.2. EQUIPMENT FOR THE WORK UNITS

The work units should be constructed in such a way that the walls, floors, and work benches can be easily washed. Louvered ceilings are definitely not allowed because dust can accumulate above them. The work benches must be provided with water, gas, and

Table 8.1. Optimal equipment in the units for water analysis

Magnetic stirrer	pH meter
Mechanical stirrer	Pumps
Sterile plastic jerry cans	Sterile glassware
Centrifuge	Material for concentration
Hood	

Table 8.2. Optimal equipment for a cell culture unit

Magnetic stirrer	Microscope
Precision balance	pH meter
Counting chamber	Refrigerators
Incubators at 37°C	Sterile Cornwall syringes
Laminar flow hood	Sterile material for cell
Material for sterilizing	cultures
filtration	Sterile glassware
Freezer to $-70°C$	CO_2 incubator

Table 8.3. Optimal equipment for an isolation and identification unit

Magnetic stirrers	Thermostatted centrifuges
Hot water bath at 37°C	Microscope
Hot water bath at 40°C	Inverse microscope
Tube holders	Refrigerator
CO_2 incubator	Sterile Cornwall syringes
Freezer to $-25°C$	Sterile glassware
Incubator at 37°C	Material for immunoenzymology
Laminar flow hood	Material for immunofluorescence

Table 8.4. Optimal equipment for a cleaning and sterilization unit

System for demineralized water	Drying chamber
Autoclave for contaminated material	Oven
Autoclave for clean material	Wrapping material
	Water basins

air or nitrogen under pressure and must be equipped with electrical sockets and overhead cabinets. A worker should find all the necessary material within arm's length. From this perspective it is sometimes necessary to provide duplicates of some pieces of equipment, such as pH meters and centrifuges.

Tables 8.1 through 8.4 present lists of equipment that should be found in each work unit.

8.3. MAINTENANCE OF THE WORK UNITS

To limit the risks of contamination, the work units should be cleaned regularly. However, cleaning should not be carried out under dry conditions such as with a broom. To prevent the moving around of dust and microorganisms, cleaning should be done under humid conditions, preferably with a disinfecting product.

Furthermore, when certain units, such as the cell culture and identification unit, are not in use, they should be maintained under ultraviolet ray tubes emitting a germicidal wavelength of 253.7 nm.

The treatment must be intense, up to 1 $W/s/cm^2$, to ensure the destruction of microorganisms as resistant as the microscopic spores of fungi. Photoelectric cells that are built for this purpose allow one to control the intensity of the germicidal rays. In the absence of this control, it is necessary to record the number of hours the lamps function and check this number against the lifetime indicated by the manufacturer. These tubes should be placed at about 1.5 to 2 meters above and, if possible, below the work tables, because germicidal effectiveness diminishes with distance. Also, regular cleaning of the tubes is essential for eliminating dust, which attenuates the intensity of the rays.

8.4. ORGANIZATION OF THE WORK UNITS

The work should be organized to avoid any contamination either from the product manipulated or from the person doing the manipulation.

8.4.1. Asepsis of the Manipulations

To avoid contaminating the products handled, it is necessary to work under relatively aseptic conditions. This calls for essential precautions in regard to the handler and the work bench.

8.4.1.1. Precautions for the Handler

The handler appears to be one of the most critical sources of contamination of the work bench because he or she constantly emits numerous microorganisms by way of the rhinopharynx and skin (Hartemann et al, 1981). For example, a cough or a loud conversation, causes the rhinopharynx of the worker to eject, numerous droplets of mucus or saliva that are very rich in bacteria. Cutaneous dissemination is due to the permanent renewing of the epidermal layer of the individual, who thusfdisperses numerous germs into the environment. These germs are maintained in suspension within several centimeters of the body because there is a warm zone around the individual. They are easily dispersed, however, by sudden movements.

To limit such risks of contamination, it is highly desirable to observe certain rules.

Be sure that each handler wears a lab coat that is tight around the wrists, as well as a mask, gloves, and a hair cover.

Use clean lab coats, which are limited if possible to each work unit and maintained under UV irradiation when not in use.

Never pipette by mouth but always use automatic pumps or hand bulbs.

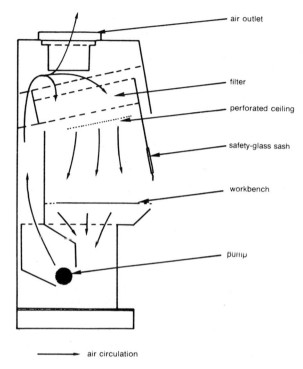

air outlet

filter

perforated ceiling

safety-glass sash

workbench

pump

⟶ air circulation

Figure 8.2. Cross-sectional schematic view of a laminar flow hood with partial recirculation of air.

8.4.1.2. Precautions at the Work Bench

To control and limit the movement of air and consequently contamination, the most elegant solution is to place the work bench under a hood with a constant descending nonturbulent flow of sterile air. Nonturbulent horizontal flows should not be allowed in virology.

Figure 8.2 offers a cross-sectional view of a nonturbulent flow hood. The aspirated air passes through a filter whose retention capacity for particles 0.3 μm in size is greater than 99.99%. The air projected in perpendicular currents is taken back through the work bench itself, then recycled.

Manipulations of cell lines and inoculations of cells should take priority for the use of nonturbulent hoods. Their verification should be done regularly by a count of the number of particles passing the filter per unit volume of air. This operation is easily conducted with the aid of particle counters.

8.4.2. Protection of the Handler

Besides accidents, the principal contaminations are produced by absorption or inhalation of a pathogenic agent or of a contaminated sample (Bordner et al, 1978). Work-related accidents and contaminations can be kept to a minimum by imposing strict rules of security on the handlers. Some examples are given.

1. Vaccinate the laboratory personnel and see that booster shots are scheduled regularly (anti-polio, anti-hepatitis B, etc).
2. Require each handler to work with a lab coat under a nonturbulent hood, with the protective glass in front of the face.
3. Require handlers to eliminate solvents under a hood.
4. Prohibit exposure of the personnel to ultraviolet rays (provide for a switch for the UV tubes outside the work place).
5. Prohibit eating, drinking, and smoking in the laboratory.
6. Require all handler to wear safety glasses during the thawing of cell cultures.
7. Avoid the use of aerosols during manipulations.

The smallest incident, such as the prick of a needle, should be noted and declared in such a way as to permit immediate intervention or, a posteriori, identification of the origin of contamination.

REFERENCES

Bordner, R., Winter, J., and Scarpino, P. V. (1978) Microbiological methods for monitoring the environment: water and wastes. U.S. Environmental Protection Agency, Report EPA-600/8-78-017, Cincinnati, OH, 354 pp.

Hartemann, P., Isoard, P., and Martin, G. (1982) L'aérobio-contamination et les problèmes généraux du traitement de l'air. In "Traitement des Effluents Liquides et Gazeux," G. Martin, Ed., Collection Point 1981. Lavoisier, Paris.

Chapter 9

CONDUCTING A VIROLOGICAL ANALYSIS

Categorizing methods of virological analysis of water systems is challenging at best. The diversity of choices shows that the available methods are both technically difficult and imperfect. Consequently, it is impossible to say that immutable procedures for the study of enteric viruses exist today.

In the sections that follow we simply propose a selection of several methods that seem to us to be acceptable, though not above reproach (Table 9.1). The proposed methodology is not unique for the whole of aqueous media. Certain steps of the analysis vary considerably, not only because final aims may vary but also because of differences in the categories of water studied.

First, we consider the problem of sampling and the transport of the samples for each type of water. Second, we indicate concentration techniques. Finally, we remark on the operations that are common to all the samples, whatever their origin: that is, the virus detection itself (inoculation into sensitive systems, etc).

9.1. SAMPLING OF WASTE WATERS

The search for viruses in wastewaters can have several aims:

On the quantitative level, the determination of the flux of viruses in wastewaters, of the effectiveness of the treatment, or of the number of viral particles discharged into the environment by human activity

On a qualitative level, the precise knowledge of the composition of the viral flora of the wastewaters

A qualitative determination permits, as part of an epidemiological study, not only knowledge of the structure of a viral population circulating in an urban community, but also a record of the appearance or disappearance of viral strains.

9.1.1. Method of Sampling

As part of a quantitative study, sampling can be carried out in different ways according to the specific aim, but it must include variations of the flux. To obtain a global evaluation of the viral population, it is necessary to carry out sampling that is adapted to the flow of the wastewaters. On the other hand, to know the hourly quantitative variations in the viral flux as a function of time, it is imperative to carry out sampling every 2 to 3 hours during the course of a 24 hour cycle.

Table 9.1. Conducting a virological analysis according to the type of water

Variable	Raw waste waters	Treated waste waters	Surface waters	Potable water
Mode of sampling	Automatic sampling as a function of water flow rate (continual or sequential)		Sampling as a function of the heterogeneity of the medium	Multiple sampling
Volume of sample	No legal guidelines		Legal guideline (EEC): 10 l	Legal guideline (WHO): 10 l
	Objective study 100 ml or 20 l 20 l		Objective study 100 l	Objective study 1000 l
Transport	As rapid as possible (+ 4°C)			
Storage	Only exceptional; less than 24 h at + 4°C			
Concentration	Absorption–elution on glass (powder or microfiber glass)			
Detection	Cell cultures (simian and human origin)			

Within the framework of a qualitative study, sampling should be carried out at the moment of maximum viral flux in a way that increases the chances of isolating different viral serotypes.

9.1.2. Volume of the Sample

The volume to be taken varies according to whether the analysis is of treated or raw wastewater.

9.1.2.1. Raw Wastewater

The detection of viruses in nontreated wastewater that is generally rich in viral particles can be carried out by inoculation onto cell cultures, either directly from the sample or from a concentrated liquid obtained from a large volume of water.

In the case of direct inoculation, a 100 ml sample is sufficient, since the inoculum is of the order of 20 to 40 ml.

In the case of a pre-concentrated sample, sample volume should lie between 10 and 20 liters.

9.1.2.2. Treated Waste Water

The viral density of treated wastewater is much smaller than that found in raw samples, and under these conditions it is not advisable to use a direct inoculation for the detection of viral particles.

Since it is acknowledged that treated wastewaters contain some viral particles almost all the time, the volume of the sample—generally 20 liters—should be increased if the search for viruses turns up negative.

9.1.3. Transport of the Sample

The sample should be analyzed as rapidly as possible after being drawn. If the duration of the transport exceeds 1 hour, it is highly advisable to keep the sample cold ($+4°C$).

If in an exceptional case, sample cannot be treated as soon as it arrives in the laboratory, it should be stored at a maximum temperature of $+4°C$ for no more than 24 hours.

9.2. SAMPLING OF SURFACE WATERS

The search for viruses in surface waters can have two objectives: sanitary on the one hand, and ecological on the other.

Investigations with a sanitary allow not only the evaluation of the virological contamination of bathing areas, but also the determination of the quality of a surface water before its treatment and transformation into water destined for human consumption. This last observation is particularly important, because a particular treatment should be modified in accordance with the results obtained.

Ecologically based virological studies are interesting because they tell what happens to viral particles discharged into the environment and afford knowledge of their behavior as a function of a certain number of parameters, such as temperature, organic matter, suspended solids, and pH.

9.2.1. Method of Sampling

Surface water quality is characterized by extreme variability. Each sequence in the sampling should be determined as a function of the spatial heterogeneity of the water system in question. To ensure an objective study, it is particularly advisable to have a preliminary study for the prupose of pinpointing the exact location (distance from the bank, depth, etc) and the frequency of the sampling, as well as the minimum number of samples.

9.2.2. Volume of the Sample

Although some guidelines designate 10 liters as the volume to be taken, an objective study that will yield meaningful results will have an optimum volume of 100 liters. This volume, however, can be reduced if the surface water to be analyzed has fecal pollution that already has been characterized.

9.2.3. Transport of the Sample

As for wastewaters, the surface water sample should be rapidly transported and, if the duration of transport exceeds 1 hour, the sample should be maintained at $+4°C$. Conservation for 24 hours at $+4°C$ should represent an exceptional case.

It is to be remarked, however, that 100 liters is the maximum practical transportable volume. For larger volumes it is necessary to proceed with the concentration of the samples directly in the field, such that only concentrated liquids with very reduced volumes are transported; alternatively, absorbant systems can be collected after the samples have been filtered. This material should be sent to the laboratory in a container maintained at 4°C.

9.3. SAMPLING POTABLE WATER

Virological analysis of potable water is of fundamental interest to public health. It permits one to determine whether a supply of water that is delivered to the public is free of viral particles. Furthermore, for studies involving drinking water treatment plants, virological analysis is very useful in evaluating the relative efficiency of the different treatment steps such as prechlorination, coagulation-flocculation, or filtration.

9.3.1. Method of Sampling

It has not been proven that the occasional or sporadic presence of viruses in potable water has an impact on the health of the consumers. On the other hand, once the presence of viruses is revealed in potable water, it is probable that consumption of this water presents some risks for the population. Under these conditions, there must be multiplicity of sampling, to support the validity of the results.

According to recommendations of the World Health Organization, water is declared potable from a virological point of view if it does not contain any enterovirus in 10 liters of water. As a matter of fact, the analysis of a 10 liter sample is entirely insufficient. In the present state of the art for these techniques, it is easy to sample and analyze 1,000 liters of water.

9.3.2. Transport of the Sample

The conditions for the transport of a 10 liter water sample are identical to those described previously (rapidity, temperature maintained at +4°C, exceptional storage for 24 hours).

As for samples of 1000 liters, transport from the place of sampling to the laboratory can be rather difficult. Under these conditions it is essential to proceed with on-site concentration of the samples.

9.4. CONCENTRATION OF THE SAMPLES

The choice of a method of concentration is difficult for two reasons. On the one hand, the physical characteristics of the samples to be analyzed can vary widely. For example, the turbidity of a water can vary from almost nil for potable water to very high in the case of wastewater. On the other hand, the methods of concentration in current use present specific advantages and inconveniences. For example, the glass microfiber technique is very simple during the adsorption phase, whereas the glass powder technique permits one to obtain a good elution of the viral particles.

From our own experience we suggest the use of concentration by adsorption-elution with its two variations: glass powder and glass microfiber. The range of application of these approaches can be determined in relation to the characteristics of the samples and, in particular, of the turbidity.

9.4.1. Very Turbid Water

Very turbid water contains by definition a large quantity of suspended matter, which might constitute the support for viral particles.

In the case of very turbid water it is recommended that the glass powder technique be used. Indeed, the presence of large quantities of matter in suspension does not trouble the passage of the sample through the fluidized bed of the glass powder. On the contrary, since this matter in suspension often provokes a rapid clogging of the glass fiber filters, their use is contraindicated. Filtration on glass fiber, with its associated phenomena of adsorption and mechanical retention, can be used nevertheless, for it allows better recuperation of the viral particles that are bound to the particles in suspension.

9.4.2. Slightly Turbid or Nonturbid Water

The glass fiber or glass powder techniques can be used indiscriminately for slightly turbid or nonturbid water. Nevertheless, for the analysis of large volumes of water and in our present state of experience, we suggest the use of glass fiber filters, first because they can be directly connected to the water pipes and second because they allow very easy concentration in the field.

9.5. DETECTION OF VIRUSES

The detection of viruses can be planned in two steps: inoculation on in vitro cell cultures and detection of viruses by immunological techniques.

Each technique has its advantages and inconveniences, which are presented in the sections that follow.

9.5.1. Detection by Inoculation on Cell Cultures

Inoculation on cell cultures can be carried out only after bacterial and fungal decontamination of the inoculum.

The detection of viruses with cell cultures is a sensitive method that permits the quantification and identification of viable viral particles only. However, this technique is relatively cumbersome and slow. As a matter of fact, taking into account different subcultures and the operations of identification and eventual intratypic differentiation, the complete virological analysis of water takes 3 to 4 weeks.

We recommend the simultaneous inoculation of two cell systems. This will serve to increase the sensitivity of the method, and the spectrum of the isolated enteric viruses will be relatively large.

The inoculation of newborn mice, specific to Coxsackie viruses, is reserved for large laboratories and cannot be recommended for routine practice.

9.5.2. Detection by Immunological Techniques

The second type of method calls on the techniques of electron microscopy, electron immunomicroscopy, and radioimmunology, immunoenzymology, and on other immunological tests.

These techniques are rapid and specific—they detect one antigenic structure only. The latter criterion, however, presents both an advantage and an inconvenience. Yet, although it is impossible to determine whether a viral particle that has been revealed is viable, the immunological methods are the only ones usable for the detection of certain viruses that are notfdeveloped on in vitro cell cultures. They can also be used for identifying viral particles that were isolated in sensitive systems.

Although these immunological methods appear to be bearers of hope for the future of virology in the medical field, they should be used with discretion in the direct virological analysis of water. Because these methods are capable of recognizing only antigenic structures, dead viruses, which are without significance to public health, will not be distinguished from live viruses.

INDEX